COMBAT
AND
SURVIVAL
WHAT IT TAKES TO FIGHT AND WIN

VOLUME
14

Originally published in the United Kingdom in weekly parts **COMBAT & SURVIVAL** is a study of the armed forces at work. It shows the skills taught to soldiers and the way in which military units operate. It examines the weapons and equipment used by different armies; and, by looking at recruit training and exercises, **COMBAT & SURVIVAL** demonstrates how the armed forces develop individual responsibility, leadership and initiative.

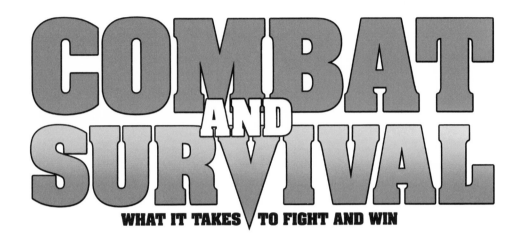

COMBAT AND SURVIVAL

WHAT IT TAKES TO FIGHT AND WIN

VOLUME
14

H. S. STUTTMAN, INC. *publishers*   Westport, Connecticut 06889

Contents

Volume 14

Published by H. S. STUTTMAN INC.
Westport, Connecticut 06889
© Aerospace Publishing 1991
ISBN 0-87475-560-3

PRINTED IN THE UNITED STATES OF AMERICA

1P(1632)30

FIRE AND MOVEMENT

You run forward with the rest of the eight-man rifle group while the machine-gun team is covering you. The mass of vegetation in your webbing must be secured so that it does not fall off once you are on the move.

5 POINTS FOR SAFE MOVEMENT

1. **Watch your Section Commander for hand signals.**
2. **Keep in contact with members of the section on each side of you — but not too close.**
3. **Keep quiet and listen for commands.**
4. **Keep in your correct position for the formation being used.**
5. **Be observant.**
6. **Be ready to change to new section formations.**

You may be fighting on a broad front, part of an engagement involving several divisions — or you may be on patrol at no more than platoon strength. However large or small the operation, the infantryman's response to events on the battlefield is centred on his Section, the most basic fighting unit in any regular army.

This part of the Combat Skills series details your tasks as a member of an Infantry Section — known in the US Army as the squad — and describes the principles of Section tactics.

The Section

In most armies this basic unit consists of between eight and 10 men (in the British Army it is eight men), one of whom is a full Corporal, the Section Commander. The section is divided

When you have reached the spot indicated by your section commander, you and the rifle group go to ground and cover the advance of the machine-gun team.

FIRE AND MOVEMENT: THE TECHNIQUE

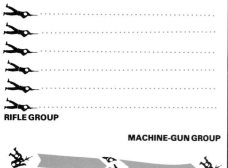

RIFLE GROUP

MACHINE-GUN GROUP

1 The gun group of two or three men advances towards the enemy under covering fire from the six to eight men in the rifle group.

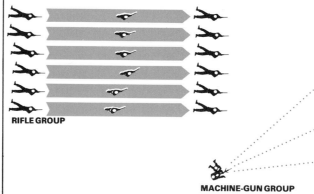

RIFLE GROUP

MACHINE-GUN GROUP

2 The machine-gun group goes to ground and opens fire: a GPMG provides enough firepower to cover the advance of the riflemen. The same principle of one unit firing while the other advances is used for pairs of riflemen, sections and whole platoons.

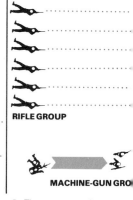

RIFLE GROUP

MACHINE-GUN GRO

3 The movement is completed by the rifle group going to ground and covering another advance by the gun group.

into a Rifle Group and Machine Gun Group. The rifle group consists of up to six riflemen, who can act in pairs or in two groups of four and two men each. The machine gun group consists of the Gunner and the Lance-Corporal in charge of the group. He is also the second-in-command of the section.

Weight of fire

There are many variations on this theme: if, for instance, a greater weight of fire is required to support an attack the machine gun group could be boosted by two extra riflemen, leaving four men to carry out the attack.

Section tactics are based on the principle of simultaneous fire and movement. Thus, if the rifle group is moving, the machine gun group should be static and ready to support – or, if necessary, actually supporting with fire – the rifle group. Clearly, the rifle group is vulnerable while on the move, and anything that can be done to keep the enemy's head down can only be helpful.

Likewise, particularly during the final stages of an assault, fire and manoeuvre will often be necessary within the rifle group itself. At the very lowest level, one member of a 'battle pair' will engage the enemy while the

Single file is the most basic formation: excellent for moving along hedges and the edges of woods, but you are vulnerable to fire from the front and few men in the section can shoot forwards.

SECTION FORMATIONS

These are the six basic formations used by an infantry section. **Single File** and **File** are easy to control but vulnerable from the front; **Arrowhead** and **Extended Line** are difficult to control, but effective against enemy in front of you. When moving in formation remember to watch your section commander for hand signals.

Arrowhead The machine-gunner is on the flank from which attack is most likely.

Single File Good for moving along the edges of woods or hedges or at night.

Extended Line Used when assaulting enemy positions.

Spearhead A variation of Arrowhead, where you don't need the machine-gun on a flank.

File Easy to control and good for night movement, but makes a good target.

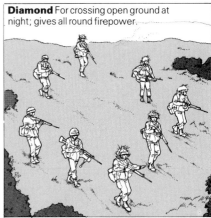

Diamond For crossing open ground at night; gives all round firepower.

other member is moving forward.

'Fire and manoeuvre' is the term given to the combined use of weapons, movement and ground. The object of fire and manoeuvre is to move with the minimum of casualties when in contact with the enemy. Suitable ground is used to protect your section from enemy fire when on the move, while fire from the static element of the section or platoon suppresses enemy fire directed at the moving element.

Supporting fire

Fire and manoeuvre is practised at all levels so that, in a major attack involving a company or battalion, a combination of supporting fire from artillery, mortar, tanks, anti-tank guided weapons (ATGW) and aircraft are used to get dismounted infantry

The General Purpose Machine Gun provides more firepower than the rest of the section put together. Everyone must be trained on both rifle and machine gun so that they can take over the GPMG if the gunner is killed or wounded.

On your feet and forward again, this time covered by one other rifleman: the members of the rifle group are paired off and work closely together. A two-man team also uses fire and movement, with one man covering the advance of the other.

2 The likely direction of enemy fire.
3 How far you can see.
4 How the Section can best be controlled.
5 The need to produce the maximum fire effect.
6 Who has control of the air.

Single File is the most basic form of military formation, and may be the only one possible in jungle. It is excellent for moving along hedges or the edge of a wood, and ideal for moving through a narrow gap in, for instance, a minefield. It is easy to control, particularly at night, and it is least vulnerable to fire from a flank. However, you are very vulnerable to frontal fire, and it is difficult to fire to your front.

Concentrated target

You can use **File** when you are moving along a path or a track that is wide enough to permit men to move on both sides of the track. Again, this formation is easy to control and useful at night, but it makes a concentrated target for enemy fire.

Arrowhead is probably the most widely used formation for moving across country. The machine gun group is put on the flank from which an attack is most likely. **Spearhead** is a variation of Arrowhead, and can be used when you don't need to deploy the gun group to one particular flank. The gun group is kept in the centre,

onto an objective.

At a much lower level, fire and manoeuvre will be used within a platoon by using one section as the fire section and the other two sections as manoeuvre groups. Similarly, fire and manoeuvre can be used within a section between individual riflemen for fighting through the enemy position.

Riflemen within a section are paired off not just so that they can fire and manoeuvre, but also so that they can help each other in a number of

other practical ways. For instance, while one member of a pair is on sentry duty, the other could be preparing a meal; or if one is wounded, the other can apply first aid.

Section formations

The basic section formations are **Single File, File, Arrowhead** or **Spearhead, Diamond** and **Extended Line**. The formation that you should adopt depends on six factors:
1 The country you are moving in.

FIELD SIGNALS ON FOOT

Hand signals are very important: it is an impossible job to shout above the noise of automatic weapons or shell fire. These signals will often be the only way your section commander can tell you something; their purpose is to get you in the right place at the right time and in the right formation. The NCO below is telling you that there is no enemy in sight.

Halt

Advance or Follow me

Close on me

Double

forming the shaft of the 'spear', ready to deploy to either flank depending on the threat. Both Arrowhead and Spearhead are good for producing effective fire against frontal attack. However, both formations are difficult to control, particularly when engaged by flanking fire.

Night movement

Diamond is often used when crossing open ground at night. It is easy to control and affords good all round observation and protection. Fire can be returned in any direction. However, it can present a concentrated target.

Extended Line can be used as an assault formation, but it is difficult to control.

Whatever formation you choose, the gun group should normally be on the open flank, or the flank that provides the best potential fire positions, such as undulating or high ground. The degree to which members of the section should be spaced out depends on the ground but, as a general rule, they should be within voice control of the section commander.

The General Purpose Machine Gun can be slung across the chest when moving and even fired from the hip in close-range firefights. But forget 'Rambo': you need to position the gun on the sling and use both hands!

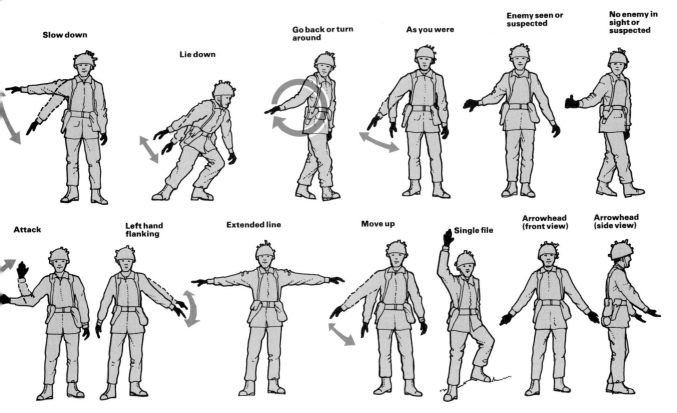

Slow down

Lie down

Go back or turn around

As you were

Enemy seen or suspected

No enemy in sight or suspected

Attack

Left hand flanking

Extended line

Move up

Single file

Arrowhead (front view)

Arrowhead (side view)

Combat Report
Malaya:
Jungle Ambush

A driver with the Royal Engineers in Singapore got more action than he bargained for when he accompanied a padre on a jungle patrol in 1952.

I entered the Army as a recruit in 1951. After finishing training in March 1952 I was posted to Singapore, where British Forces were having to deal with student riots. I was soon posted to Johore Bahru as a padre's driver. The padre liked nothing better than to get out with the troops: he decided to go into the jungle on a five-day patrol with the Somerset Light Infantry, and asked me to take him up to Kota Tinggi camp.

"When do you want me to pick you up again?" I asked.

"Pick me up? You're coming with me!"

"No, thank you, sir. I don't fancy that."

"You're coming with me! That's an order!"

Early next morning, just as it got light, I went to the armoury and drew out my Sten gun and six mags of 30 rounds of ammo, then picked up the padre at the officers' mess. We drove to Kota Tinggi, reported to the patrol commander and got checked over, then off we went down the track and into the deep, impenetrable jungle with the patrol.

One went down with malaria

Almost immediately we had to hack our way through, the leading scouts cutting a path; we were being eaten alive by insects, and all sorts of weird noises were assailing our ears. Within minutes we were soaked to the skin with sweat and water from the trailing vegetation.

The Somerset Light Infantry lads were grinning broadly at the sight of the padre striding along the path. He was in his best jungle greens and was wearing his normal service cap, which after a while he was persuaded to remove and put on a jungle hat, which wasn't so conspicuous.

We had been out for about two days without any contact when we came to a clearing with a lot of tracks leading in and out of it. The Dyak tracker who was with the patrol stated, "Men use track recently." It was decided to set up an

A Daimler armoured car ventures up a jungle road at the head of a vehicle column. Road convoys had to be protected from guerrilla ambush.

ambush position in the clearing and surrounding tracks.

As the ambush was being set, one of the soldiers went down with malaria. This meant that the section was short for stag duties. The sergeant came up to me and said, "I know you're only here for the ride and you're non-combatant, but as everyone in the Army is basically a soldier and should know how to defend himself and his mates, would you be so kind as to take that fool's place in the section? He hasn't been taking his anti-malaria pills."

All this came as a bit of a shock, but he asked so nicely that I couldn't refuse. "OK, Sarge."

"Thanks," he said. "You won't be so willing when you know which stag you've got – it's the death watch, 0400 to 0600 hours." This is stand-to time, and the time when most enemy attacks take place.

When I was called, I took up my stag position, behind a large tree overlooking a track with thick jungle on the far side. As I settled down, my mind began to wander to thoughts of home, girlfriend, and how long I had to do in Malaya.

Suddenly I was brought back with a jolt by a very loud crack from the other side of the clearing, sounding like a piece of wood being carelessly trodden on. I was instantly up on my feet with most of my body behind the tree, and my Sten gun trained across the clearing with the safety catch off. The moon was shining, bathing the clearing in bright light; the jungle on my side was pitch black.

His fatal mistake

As I listened, wondering if it was a human or an animal, I could hear movement coming towards me. Not daring to call out to the next sentry, I remained still and quiet. Then I heard the sound of cloth being torn or scratched by thorns, followed by muttering – presumably swearing – in Chinese. Then I waited.

After about two minutes the bushes on the far side of the clearing gently parted and a white blob, a face, peered through.

The person had a very good look round for about five minutes. Then he moved out to the very edge of the clearing and stood there looking and listening, up and down the tracks. After another few minutes he decided it was safe to move into the clearing proper. As he moved he brought his rifle up into the alert

A British officer and members of a platoon of local troops, ready to search the jungle for Communist terrorists.

position. He was wearing a cap, and the outline of Red Star stood out in the moonlight.

I waited until he was very close to the edge of the jungle and almost in front of me, then I eased myself out from the tree's cover so that I could, if need be, get a better shot at him. Anyway, he must have been well on his guard, because he saw me moving and brought his rifle round in my direction.

I shouted "Halt!" and he realised his fatal mistake: as I opened fire, he was attempting to load his rifle.

We opened his pack

As I emptied my mag at him, I saw I was hitting him all over his body and it was only the click of my gun on an empty mag that stopped me. I stood in the open, looking down in shock at the body sprawled at my feet. I heard shouts behind me, and realised that I had killed a fellow human being. I just stood over him and, without knowing what I was doing, shouted at the top of my voice, "I've killed him; I've killed him; I've killed the ******* bastard!"

The next thing I remember is the platoon sergeant smacking me round the face and rugby-tackling me back into the jungle and saying, "Get back and get down, you prat – there could be more out there. Reload your bloody gun and stand by."

Well, we waited there in stand-to readiness until well past first light, then the officers sent a section out to flank the far side of the jungle and sweep through to the clearing, keeping in contact by radio so we wouldn't open fire on them. When they completed their sweep and came out of the jungle on the far side, we moved out from our side with safety catches on. While some of the sections kept guard, we moved up to the body and made sure it was not booby-trapped. Then we took off his pack and opened it.

We thought we had won the jackpot on the local lottery: thousands of dollars spilled out. We realised he was a collector for the Party – an important person.

After that it was all routine. The helicopter was called in and the body removed for ID. We carried on to finish the patrol, then returned to Johore Bahru. The news soon travelled round the camp that I had got a Commie.

Combat Skills

PREPARE FOR BATTLE

Faced with the task of leading a section out through hostile country and taking out an enemy position, what do you do? How should you prepare for the mission? How will you react to enemy fire, or even find the enemy in the first place? And how will you mount a successful assault?

There are, in fact, six logical steps – 'battle drills' – that you are trained to follow on such an operation. In the heat of battle it's not always possible to stick slavishly to the rules, but the six drills for a section likely to come under enemy fire give you a tried and tested framework on which to hang your plan of action.

1: Preparing for battle

Before advancing to contact you must first check that your personal camouflage is correct. It should break up the outline of the helmet, equipment and the outline of your body by using scrim, faceveil and suitable foliage representative of the ground over which the section is about to

6 SECTION DRILLS

1. Prepare weapons and equipment.
2. React quickly to enemy fire.
3. Locate the enemy's position.
4. Win the firefight.
5. Assault under covering fire.
6. Re-organise the section.

Opening fire with a Self-Loading Rifle: it is difficult to control the shooting of a 10-man section, but your firepower must be co-ordinated if it is to be effective. British soldiers practise fighting in pairs, one providing covering fire as the other advances. Conducted with live ammunition, it fosters confidence and teamwork, as well as good shooting.

Before battle you must prepare your personal camouflage and check your weapon and ammunition. This American soldier needs to add plenty of local foliage to break up his shape.

GETTING ON TARGET

One of the biggest problems in controlling the firepower of the section is getting everyone to fire at the correct target. When indicating a target to the rest of the section, shout out the range (e.g. '300'); the direction (e.g. ¾ left); and any obvious point of reference (e.g. 'gate') – so the call is '300 – ¾ left – gate'.

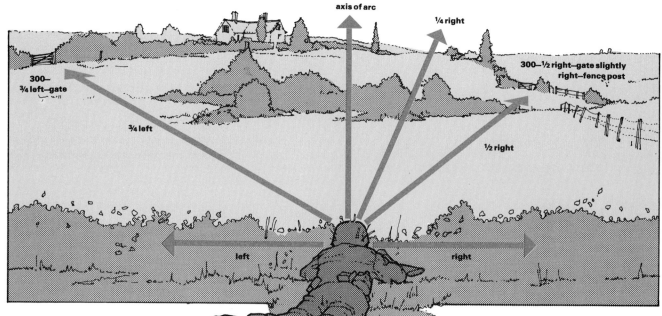

operate. Your weapon must be clean, serviceable and well oiled. Ammunition must be clean and magazines and grenades properly distributed throughout the section. The radio operator must ensure that he is properly in touch with platoon headquarters.

As section commander you must prepare and deliver your orders before the section starts out on the operation. Those orders should ensure that all members of the section know as much as possible about the nature of the ground they are about to cross, the likely weapons and dispositions of the enemy, and the location, intentions and tasks of the rest of the platoon and company. Everyone must know what his mission is and how he is going to carry it out.

You will give everyone details of the route, the formations the section will be using, which flank the machine gun group should go on and any other relevant details. As the sec-

The firepower of the section must be controlled by the commander. Here a US squad leader directs the fire of an M203 grenade-launcher mounted on an M16A1.

tion advances to contact, you will give your anticipatory fire orders: "If we come under fire go to ground along that bank," and so on. All the details come under the heading of 'Preparation for Battle'.

2: Reacting to effective enemy fire

Sections must be trained to carry on advancing regardless of the noise of fire directed at someone else and re-gardless of stray rounds. Effective enemy fire, on the other hand, is fire that would cause heavy casualties if the section continued on its course.

The immediate reaction to effective fire must be for the whole section to get off the killing ground immediately. If you have been able to give anticipatory orders, the section will know exactly where to take cover. If not, they must listen to orders and crawl into the nearest available cover. Every

If you come under fire, get out of the killing ground immediately; go to ground and return fire. You must understand the importance of fire control and avoid unnecessary expenditure of ammunition.

man must try to establish where the enemy fire is coming from — and return it.

The drill for getting off the killing ground is:
1 Dash
2 Down
3 Crawl
4 Observe
5 Sights
6 Fire!

3: Locating the enemy

Locating the position from which someone is firing at you can be very difficult, particularly in a built-up area. Clearly, you have to locate the enemy as soon as possible, in order both to continue to advance and to prevent casualties. There are three methods of finding the enemy:
1 By observation If you look in the direction from which you think the sound of the fire came, you may see movement, smoke, muzzle flashes, or something glinting. There are two components to the sound of a shot: a 'crack', which is the round passing you; and a 'thump', which is the explosion in the chamber of the rifle.

The time between the crack and the thump gives an indication of range — each second represents about 600 metres.

CLOCK RAY METHOD

To identify more difficult targets to the rest of the section you can use the Clock Ray method. Give the same reference as before, but refer to an imaginary clock over one of the reference points. To refer to the hedges to the left of the house in the diagram you shout: '300-half left-7 o'clock-hedge'. If someone is pointing out a target to you, shout 'Seen' or 'Not seen' as appropriate.

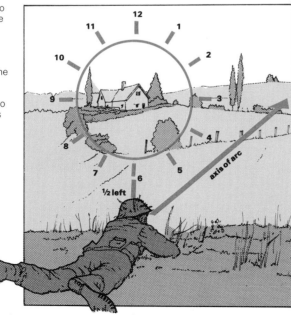

Combat Skills

It is not always possible to give a rapid indication of the enemy position. Here a soldier fires a tracer round at the enemy – a quick way of identifying an area, but it tends to give away your own position.

2 By fire You can try to draw the enemy's fire by instructing perhaps two riflemen to fire into likely cover.
3 By movement If the enemy has still not been spotted, you will have to order two men to get up and run forward about 10 metres to a different position. This will almost certainly draw enemy fire, but don't worry. A man getting up and dashing 10 metres is a very hard target to hit.

Finally, if there is still no enemy reaction, you must continue to advance.

Anyone who spots the enemy must indicate the position to his comrades by firing a round of tracer at the enemy position.

4: Winning the fire fight

As soon as the enemy has been firmly located, you must bring down a sufficient weight of fire on the enemy to neutralise him. Having won the fire fight, you must maintain a sufficient weight of fire with the machine gun group to allow your rifle group to move to a position from which it can assault the enemy.

5: The attack

The attack consists of four stages:
1 Orders The section commander issues brief orders so that each rifleman knows exactly what he is to do. Moreover, the machine gun group, which will usually stay behind to provide covering fire, must be clear about precisely what is going to happen *before* the rifle group departs on its flanking attack.
2 The advance The aim of this stage is to move from the position where the section first came under fire to a suitable position from which to assault the enemy. In order to make an angle as near 90 degrees as possible between the supporting fire of the gun group and the assault position of the rifle group, most advances will be to a flank.

In certain circumstances, it might be best to move the gun group to a flank and advance forward on the same axis – if, for instance, there is some 'dead ground' directly in front of the enemy.
3 The assault Attacking troops normally need a superiority in the region of three to one. Therefore a section, by definition, is capable of attacking only a single trench, a sniper or a pill box. If

JUDGING DISTANCE: THE 100-METRE METHOD

The range is the first detail you must give when identifying a target to the section, and you should practise judging distances so that you can do so quickly and confidently. A full-size football pitch is about 100 metres long. Once you can visualise this distance, use it as a unit of measurement between you and the target.

Familiar objects
Learn what familiar objects like trucks or houses look like at different ranges. This will help you judge the distance.

Things seem further away
1 When you have the sun in your eyes.
2 In bad light.
3 When you are looking down a street or over a valley.
4 When they are smaller than their surroundings.
5 If you are lying down.

Things seem closer
1 In bright sunshine.
2 If they are bigger than their surroundings.
3 If they are higher than you.
4 If there is dead ground between you and them.

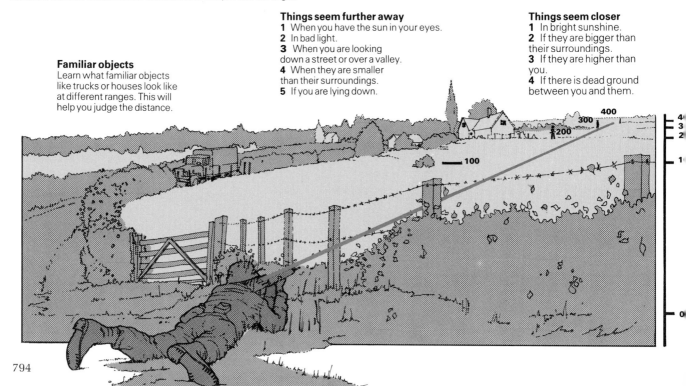

you find that you are faced with opposition much stronger than this, call in any available reinforcements.

The assault is the final stage of the advance on the enemy position. The maximum fire must be brought to bear at this stage from both the assaulting rifle group and the supporting machine gun group. Fragmentation grenades can be thrown, or you can fire the section's light or medium anti-tank weapon to create the maximum shock. Smoke grenades can be thrown to cover the assaulting riflemen over the last few yards.

This is the most difficult part of an attack for the section commander: you have to coax your men to get up from a

A captured Argentine position. If possible, reorganise a little way off as the enemy may have pre-registered artillery on the position.

secure fire position and charge, with bayonets fixed, across probably open ground to close with and kill the enemy. It is no mean task.

4 Fighting through The position may be sited in depth. Once committed, the section must maintain the momentum by using fire and man-oeuvre to capture the whole position, or the assault may collapse.

6: Reorganising your section

As soon as you have neutralised the enemy position, you must organise your section as quickly as possible, to

You are very vulnerable in the moments after taking the enemy position, and immediate re-organisation is essential. Deal with casualties, check ammo state and dig in if necessary.

be ready for a possible counter-attack.

You must allot arcs of fire to each man, deal with casualties, redistribute ammunition and, if necessary, dig trenches or shell-scrapes. The gun group must regroup on the position as quickly as possible.

White phosphorus grenades are horribly effective in close-quarter fighting. Lighter than a fragmentation grenade, you can throw them further and more accurately.

Combat Report

Corsica:
French Foreign Legion in Calvi

The French Foreign Legion has been stationed on Corsica for the last 25 years. There is an uneasy truce between the Legion and the FLN (National Liberation Front of Corsica).

In 1983 there were some shootings and bomb attacks on the island, and the government decided to take some action. My section was airlifted to Corsica, where we were tasked to the mountains north of Calvi to search for any signs of terrorist activity.

One day, we had been out since early morning and decided to stop for a bite to eat. I took one of the men with me to a hotel to buy some beer and sandwiches. As we approached, two men came out of the front door; as soon as they saw us they turned around and went back in again. Something told me to be careful. I looked around, but could see nothing.

To the left, a car started up with a young woman behind the wheel. As I continued on my way, a shot rang out. I dived behind some gables and tried to see where it had come from.

A shot rang out

It was obvious that the two men who had gone back into the hotel had had something to do with it, so I told my mate to cover me and ran to the front door. When I got there I motioned him forward. We entered the hotel, rifles at the ready; the foyer was empty. I remembered the car outside and ran to the door: just as I reached it, it pulled away. There were three or four people in it, and it was a sure bet that the two men I'd seen earlier were passengers.

By this time the four other Legionnaires in the group had arrived. They tried to stop the car, but it drove straight at them and they were forced to jump out of the way. Luckily one of them managed to get a shot at it, and it crashed about 100 metres up the road. As we approached, more shots rang out and we had to take cover, but fortunately they weren't very accurate and stopped as soon as we returned fire.

We advanced slowly. The car was empty apart from a 9-mm pistol and a small bag containig documents. Two of my men went round the back and found a woman lying in a ditch. She was crying her eyes out and bleeding from a gunshot wound to the leg. I asked her where her passengers were but she wouldn't answer.

Meanwhile I had called for assistance, and it wasn't long before a Gendarmerie mobile patrol

Anti-terrorist patrols are ferried to the operational area by helicopter. This gives the enemy less warning than a road move.

turned up and told me another unit was on its way. I handed the woman over to them and told them I was going after the others.

We moved along the road in fighting formation. There was a crossroads up ahead, and I had a horrible feeling that something was going to happen there so I sent a man up ahead and told him to let himself be seen while we did a detour. We got across OK, and headed back down towards him. As we came up to him a shot rang out. We all hit the deck, and I shouted, "Is anyone hit?" Everyone called back, "No". I then ordered two men to cover us while we moved to safer positions. There was a stone wall by the road, so we headed for that.

Peering over, I saw a ridge line that disappeared round a bend. They were obviously expecting us to walk round the bend and straight into their trap. Well, I had other plans. I told one man to go to the bend while the rest of us went up on to the ridge line and tried to outflank them. He gave us five minutes to get up above him, then he started moving towards the bend.

As he got there, another shot rang out. This time we saw where it came from. We returned fire while making our way towards the gunman. More shots cracked around us, this time from another position. Now I could see what was going on: they were using one man to keep our heads down while the others made some distance; then they would take cover and fire at us while he made his way back. And they were doing it rather well!

They threw a grenade

I signalled to our man on the road to join us. I scanned the map and saw a track that led into the mountains: this was probably their escape route. I decided to head for it and maybe cut one of them off.

We spread out and started running towards the track. Two men could just be seen, higher up the mountain. They had been walking as if they were out for a stroll until they saw us! Suddenly they took off, with us in pursuit. I fired, but they were out of range. We reached the track and I left two men to keep guard.

Then the four of us headed up the steep, winding track. We climbed for about ten minutes until we came to some very large boulders. I climbed up on to one of these and could see the two men moving about below, so I took aim and fired. They took cover, and bullets whizzed over my head.

I climbed down and we continued up the track, which was getting steeper. The firing started again and we moved from rock to rock, exchanging fire. Sometimes we could see them moving about. At one stage they threw a

grenade; I thought it was a bird flying over, until it exploded!

Suddenly there was a long burst of fire, and we had to keep our heads well down. Just as suddenly, it stopped, but we didn't raise our heads in case it was a false alarm. After a couple of minutes we moved forward again and stumbled upon their firing position. They'd gone, but in their haste they had left a pair of binoculars and a full magazine. One of my men went to pick it up, but I stopped him: it could have been booby-trapped. Attaching a length of string, I told everyone to take cover. I gave it a tug and nothing happened, so I gave another tug and up it went, the bullets going off all over the place.

We checked the surrounding area and found nothing. Then we continued along the track, which finally petered out into a small footpath. I decided that to go along this would be inviting trouble, and that we had done our bit for today.

Then I heard firing coming from where I had left the two Legionnaires, so we hurried back to help them. Fortunately they had everything under control, with one dead terrorist lying on the track. He had walked straight into them and had fired when they challenged him. They had fired back, killing him instantly. We wrapped him in a poncho and carried him down the mountain to the main road.

When we got there we found that the police and other Legionnaires had arrived. I told them what had happened, and they took up the search and moved off. We headed back to Calvi.

I felt proud of the way my men had acted. We had worked as a team, and had come through unscathed. The two men who had shot the terrorist were a bit subdued, which was to be expected. But it was beers all round that night.

Sentry removal the Legion way. A scoped hunting crossbow will kill as quickly and quietly as a knife if the shot is correctly placed.

Legionnaires on parade, complete with Famas and bayonets: a contrast to the hard slog of hunting terrorists hidden in remote areas.

TACTICAL MOVEMENT

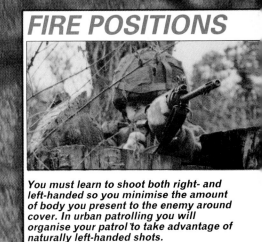

You must learn to shoot both right- and left-handed so you minimise the amount of body you present to the enemy around cover. In urban patrolling you will organise your patrol to take advantage of naturally left-handed shots.

Good tactical movement is largely common sense. However, in most situations you will not have time to ponder your next move. You must develop your skills so that you instinctively know what will work and what is going to get you killed.

"If it feels right – do it," said the actress to the bishop, and that's sound advice too for applying techniques of tactical movement. The various methods of walking, rolling and crawling in combat taught by the British Army today all have their names and approved styles, dating from World War II, but they're not holy writ. The main thing is to do the right thing in the circumstances.

Before you move at all, the first thing to do when going out on patrol is check your equipment. Make sure you can reach your ammunition when you're lying prone. Ideally, pouches should be halfway between your belt buckle and your hips. Tape down anything that might rattle or catch the light. Take care you've no loops or buckles that will catch on vegetation. Get snarled up on a hedge and you'll make a fine target.

Hands, knees and feet

To move behind low cover, use the Monkey Run – it's a fast way to move on hands and knees. Lower cover calls for the Leopard Crawl. Lie flat out on the ground and push yourself forward with the edges of your feet, your elbows and forearms. Keeping absolutely flat during the Leopard Crawl can be tricky. There's a tendency to keep head, chest and feet down, but to stick your behind in the air. This looks comical enough, but the hazards are worse!

Both these movements are hard on your limbs, and on rocky ground will wear out your kit as well. Take care to keep dirt out of your rifle muzzle when crawling. The best way is to loop the sling through the joint of the thumb and index finger and so pull the weapon along with you.

To get away from a skyline, roll. And don't flail your arms and legs about – roll "at attention", so to speak, with your rifle close to your body. If

When you are in contact with the enemy you must carefully select each fire position. Never shoot over cover like this if you can shoot through or round it.

Combat Skills

for some reason you can't roll, lower your head slowly – a sudden movement will only attract notice. Then back away slowly. Bending at the knees while doing so will make you seem smaller.

Heavy weapons

The Army's new 5.56-mm weapons have made the infantryman's load lighter and movement easier, but crew-served weapons like the GPMG and MAW are still a handful. You may also have to hump the 84-mm Carl Gustav and its ammunition, as well as your own personal weapon. The load can be considerable. The No. 1 can either sling the weapon under his right arm and drag it alongside in the Side Crawl, or cradle the weapon in both arms in the Leopard Crawl. Take care of the optic sights in either crawl.

The improved version of the Carl Gustav weighs in about the same as a GPMG, is made of lightweight steel, carbon fibre and alloys, and has a carrying handle at the point of balance. It's thus a far more practical weapon – but it is not in service with the British Army.

The GPMG is a voracious eater of ammunition if you use it to suppress a position, and both crew and section will need to carry its linked 7.62-mm ammunition with them wherever they go. To move with the weapon you can use the side and knee crawls. In the former, the gunner holds the weapon by the carrying handle in his right hand, while his feet and left elbow push him forward. You can move faster but more obviously with the knee crawl. The gunner half-kneels

and uses one hand for support and the other for the GPMG. The No. 1 and No. 2 can work together with one holding the butt and the other the bipod as they move forward in a Leopard Crawl. Keep the ammunition clear of dirt to prevent malfunctions.

The GPMG should be carried in the alert position by the gunner when the unit is in the advance to contact. In this way he looks like an ordinary rifleman at a distance and does not attract fire before he has had a chance to bring the weapon into action.

In Arctic conditions, carry crew-served weapons on pulks (small sledges). Weapons like the LMG can be fired if the bipod legs are secured to snow shoes or light support like underbrush.

Night moves

You must move silently at night. For this, use the Ghost Walk. Lift your legs high, sweeping them slowly and gently outwards and then putting them carefully down. As you do this, use the toes to detect any loose twigs that would break under pressure. If you start by putting the outer edge of

THE MONKEY RUN

This is a good method of moving behind low cover at speed. Keep your head up and keep looking round, not just at where you are going to put your hands. Always use your knuckles rather than the open hand as injuries to your palm may prevent you from using your rifle. If you hold the weapon off the ground against your side and use just one hand you are doing the side crawl, which is usually used with heavier weapons such as the GPMG.

THE LEOPARD CRAWL AND KITTEN CRAWL

Left: The leopard crawl is used for low cover and involves using alternate knees and elbows. The common mistakes are not observing forward and not keeping your backside down so that it becomes a target in itself.

Below: The kitten crawl is for very low cover when in close contact with the enemy. You move forward using only your hands and feet. Note the use of the sling swivel to carry the rifle out of the mud.

your foot down first, and then roll the sole across until it is flat on the ground, you will reduce the danger of breaking branches or slipping.

The Cat Walk is similar to the Monkey Run, but slower. You use your hands to feel forward for obstructions and also to check the ground for branches. Put your knee in the place that has been checked by your hand.

The Kitten Crawl is very slow and also very quiet. You start prone and use your elbows and toes to lift yourself up and forward, and then lower yourself gently down.

While moving at night, allow time to listen. Stop and look towards the areas you wish to check by ear – sometimes it helps to have your mouth slightly open. And stay near the ground, even if this is just squatting or hunching your back. You will see objects or people silhouetted against the sky. If you put your ear close to dry ground you will hear the vibration of vehicles or feet.

As you close with an enemy position you will encounter his obstacle belts. These may be merely trip flares put forward of the position, or barbed

wire and mines. Slow down and take things carefully. Feel forward with your hands and finger tips – trip wires can be detected by touch.

The "Ghost Man" – so named because of his silent work and his life expectancy – works his way forward with a thin wand of wood just brushing through the undergrowth. A trip wire will stop the wand, but the stick is too light to trip the wire. You can then disarm the mine or flare.

The darkness will heighten your senses, so use your ears and nose as well as your sense of touch. You may

THE ROLL

The roll is used to move away from ridgelines where you would be silhouetted if you stood up. Note that the weapon is held firmly against the side of the body.

FIRE AND MANOEUVRE

direction of advance

Pairs

Tactical movement in contact with the enemy relies on efficient use of firepower to cover movement. The Small Arms 80 weapon system has had a significant effect on tactics. The eight-man section, armed with two LSW, selective fire rifles and LAW 80, permits a great deal more flexibility in how the section can be used. The section of eight men should be seen as four pairs which can be combined in different ways to make up two fireteams.

Fire teams

The fireteam or "brick" is the smallest effective tactical unit. You can combine pairs A and C and B with D to produce balanced fire teams so that each team can act as assault group or fire support. Since the flanking attack has largely fallen from favour, this grouping is the better option for the attack.

Gun group, rifle group (right)

In FIBUA and some CRW operations it will make sense to have a gun group and a rifle group. What you can do here is put your two LSWs together with a GPMG SF team detached from platoon HQ to fire some serious fire support. This allows you to make up an assault group of two three-man teams.

WANDING TRIPWIRES

At night you could easily blunder into tripwires left by the enemy to detect you or just to inflict casualties. They may trigger anything from a flare to an 1,000-lb bomb.

Use a 'wanding' stick to feel for trip wires in likely areas such as tracks, rides or known enemy positions.

Fire support and manoeuvre group (left)
Alternatively you can put A with D and B with C to make a fire support team with both LSWs and an assault group or manoeuvre group with all the riflemen. The pairs system will allow you to change formation quickly.

800

GHOST WALK

The ghost walk is used at night when moving through close cover near the enemy. It is very slow and involves completely checking over the next space you are moving into.

Feel forward for anything that might snag on your equipment and break, making a noise. Start at head height and move down.

Check where you are going to tread for twigs or anything you could fall over. At night, your fingers are your eyes!

Stop and listen often. Turn your head and keep your mouth open: it will help you pick up sound.

hear or smell your enemy before you see him. Remember, he may do the same to you if you do not take the right precautions.

By day or night, however, you should try to choose the best route making use of the terrain. Hedges, gullies and drainage ditches, walls, woods and buildings will screen you from the enemy. But remember that cover from view is not cover from fire – a hedge is not bullet proof and nor are a fence or even light walls or buildings.

Look for cover

As you move, keep an eye open for possible cover, as well as possible enemy locations. Thus if a tree line looks like a potential enemy position look for the cover that is reasonably close. If you come under effective enemy fire the last thing you will want to do is to dash a long way in the open. However, isolated cover should be avoided – a single tree in an open field is very obvious and the enemy gunner or section can all see it when given a target indication.

When you have gone to ground remember to crawl or roll away – if the enemy has seen you go down he will surely keep an eye on the position and wait to shoot you when your head pops up.

Movement by day or night, under fire or out of contact will become a matter of instinct. You will adapt variants of different walks and crawls as they fit the terrain or tactical situation. If it feels right – do it.

FIRE AND MANOEUVRE

Good tactical movement will mean you will not give your position away to the enemy until you are in a position to do some damage. Once he knows where you are you have to think about cover from view and fire, and use fire to cover any movement as these rebel Filippino soldiers are doing. One fires his M14 as the other prepares to move forward on the TV station in Manila defended by soldiers loyal to the Marcos regime.

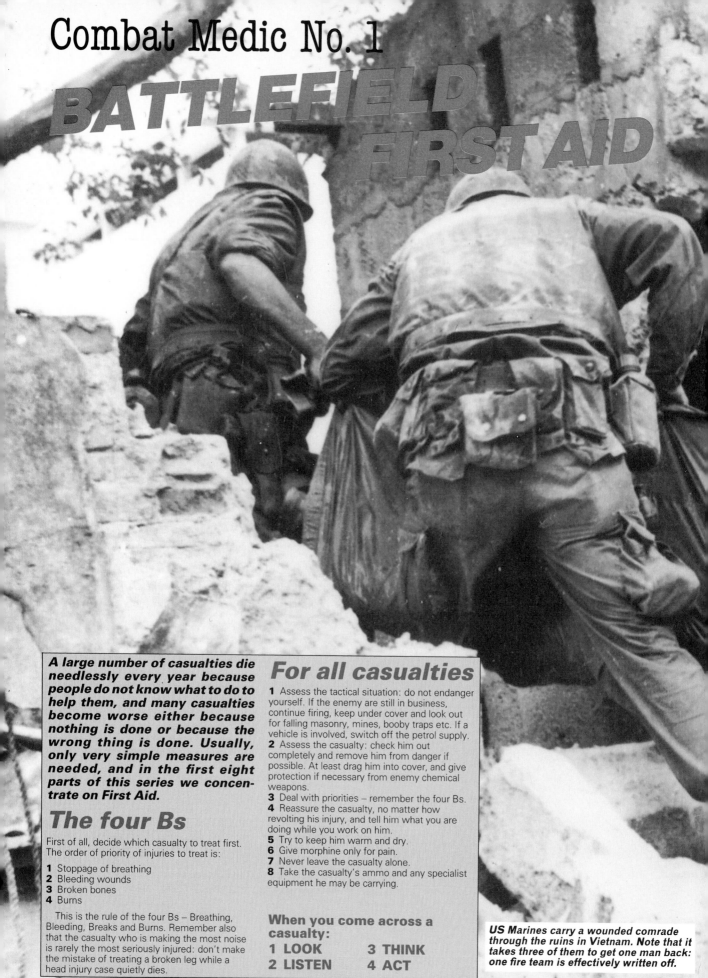

Combat Medic No. 1
BATTLEFIELD FIRST AID

A large number of casualties die needlessly every year because people do not know what to do to help them, and many casualties become worse either because nothing is done or because the wrong thing is done. Usually, only very simple measures are needed, and in the first eight parts of this series we concentrate on First Aid.

The four Bs

First of all, decide which casualty to treat first. The order of priority of injuries to treat is:

1 Stoppage of breathing
2 Bleeding wounds
3 Broken bones
4 Burns

This is the rule of the four Bs – Breathing, Bleeding, Breaks and Burns. Remember also that the casualty who is making the most noise is rarely the most seriously injured: don't make the mistake of treating a broken leg while a head injury case quietly dies.

For all casualties

1 Assess the tactical situation: do not endanger yourself. If the enemy are still in business, continue firing, keep under cover and look out for falling masonry, mines, booby traps etc. If a vehicle is involved, switch off the petrol supply.
2 Assess the casualty: check him out completely and remove him from danger if possible. At least drag him into cover, and give protection if necessary from enemy chemical weapons.
3 Deal with priorities – remember the four Bs.
4 Reassure the casualty, no matter how revolting his injury, and tell him what you are doing while you work on him.
5 Try to keep him warm and dry.
6 Give morphine only for pain.
7 Never leave the casualty alone.
8 Take the casualty's ammo and any specialist equipment he may be carrying.

When you come across a casualty:

1 LOOK   3 THINK
2 LISTEN   4 ACT

US Marines carry a wounded comrade through the ruins in Vietnam. Note that it takes three of them to get one man back: one fire team is effectively written off.

First Aid in Combat

If you get hit, sort yourself out if you can. Otherwise, whoever gets to you first will help you. In a tactical situation, lightly wounded men can carry on fighting after being given first aid, and must be encouraged to do so.

Each section contains a combat medic who is trained in combat first aid: he is, however, primarily a rifleman and may well become a casualty himself. So you must all not only know the life-saving techniques, but must be practised in their use. There is nothing worse than watching one of your mates die because you don't have the skill or the knowledge to save him.

Dealing with a casualty while in contact with the enemy will be covered in the orders issued before every operation. But the following applies in general to various phases of war:

The attack

Once you are across the effective fire line, winning the firefight and fire-and-manoeuvring forward, you cannot afford to stop. If someone gets hit and you are near him there is a strong temptation to go and help, especially if he is making a lot of noise. The result is that more and more people are drawn into casualty handling, less fire goes down on the enemy, and his fire gets heavier and more accurate.

As more people get hit, you lose the firefight and the attack fails. Withdrawing from the EFL is as expensive as fighting through, so you might as well remove the source of injury by killing the enemy and let your reserve platoons give first aid as they move up behind you.

Most first aid will be given during Reorganisation at the end of the attack.

Patrols

Casualties incurred on the route out will be left with a guard, if your patrol has sufficient strength, and the standby patrol tasked to collect them. If you're on the route back, you take your casualties with you. If you're in contact with the enemy, you must take your casualties back with you as you break contact. If you are going to leave them, you must be 100 per cent sure that they are dead.

Generally, recce patrols will not be large enough to take many casualties and go on with the mission. Fighting patrols are intended for combat and are therefore large enough to take casualties.

Defence

If someone in a four-man main battle trench gets hit, one of the others gives first aid while the remaining two continue to fire. If, however, the enemy has closed to within grenade-chucking distance, it is not a good idea for anyone to stop firing.

Do not move around the position to help other trenches unless you have dug communication trenches. Forward slope positions are very difficult to move casualties back from, compared to reverse slope. The best approach is to carry out immediate first aid in situ and make the casualty as comfortable as possible in the shelter bay until rounds stop flying.

Internal security

The terrorist or insurgent uses casualties to create more casualties; he will aim to injure or kill one man or unit to draw the remainder into an ambush, command-detonated mines or a sniper. Watch out!

A convincing-looking casualty on exercise. Since the Falklands, more effort has been put into training for war and on realistic casualty-handling.

CLEARING THE AIRWAY

Signs of an obstructed airway or choking are noisy, bubbling, gasping or whistling breathing or blueness of the face. *Unless you act quickly, the casualty will die.* Kneel by his side and tilt his head back, and remove any tight clothing round his neck.

Clear out anything in his mouth that is obstructing his airway, such as vomit or broken teeth. He should start breathing at this point.

When carrying out first aid, remember the four Bs — Breathing, Bleeding, Breaks and Burns. You must deal with breathing first, because if a casualty has an obstructed airway and cannot breathe he will die, however well you treat his other injuries.

The human brain starts to suffer permanent damage after about four minutes without oxygen, so you must get a casualty breathing again as quickly as you can.

Check his mouth

A casualty with an obstructed airway may have stopped breathing completely, but you are more likely to find him choking. First, look into the casualty's mouth and extract anything obstructing his throat. You must not be squeamish: remove whatever is there, even if it is covered with blood or vomit. Be positive, and don't fiddle about.

Obstructing tongue

Sometimes the tongue can fall back and block the throat. You clear the casualty's airway by extending his neck: with him flat on his back, tilt his head right back. If he doesn't start to breathe then you must resuscitate him; otherwise, treat him as an unconscious casualty.

Causes of obstruction

There are five main causes of an obstructed airway:

1 Suffocation
2 Teeth, including false teeth
3 Swelling of the mouth or throat
4 Blood, water or vomit
5 Bone or tissue injuries

If the casualty is unconscious, tuck his nearside hand under his body and the other over his chest. Cross the far foot over the nearer one. Then, supporting his head with one hand, grasp his clothing on his hip and roll him towards you.

Check that his airway remains clear and make sure that he cannot roll right over onto his front and that his neck stays extended. By placing him in this position his airway will stay clear even if he vomits, and he will not swallow his tongue.

How to treat an unconscious casualty

You must place an unconscious casualty in such a position that no further harm will come to him. An unattended, unconscious casualty can easily die by choking to death on his own vomit. To keep his airway clear, place him in the recovery position.

Left: Check his pulse every 15 minutes and examine the rest of his body for obvious injuries. Remember that anyone with neck or spinal injuries cannot be moved, and you will need further assistance. Casevac an unconscious casualty as soon as you can, and never leave him alone.

RESUSCITATION TECHNIQUES

How to perform artificial resuscitation

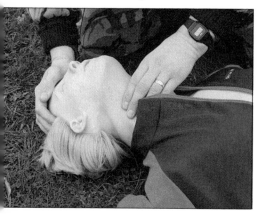

Check the casualty's pulse at his carotid artery. If his heart has stopped, you will need to perform cardiac compression as well as resuscitation.

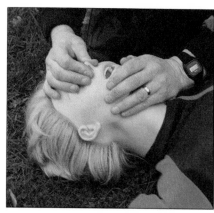

To perform resuscitation, place the casualty on his back and extend his neck by tilting his head back. Check his airway and remove any obstructions.

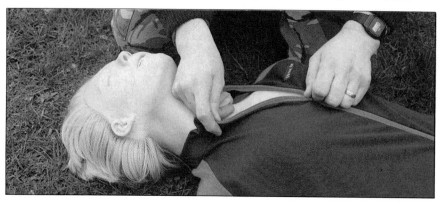

Above: Loosen any tight clothing around his neck.
Below: Pinch his nose, take a deep breath and breathe hard into his mouth, hard enough to make his chest rise. Then remove your mouth and allow his chest to fall. Repeat every six seconds, and continue until he begins to breathe.

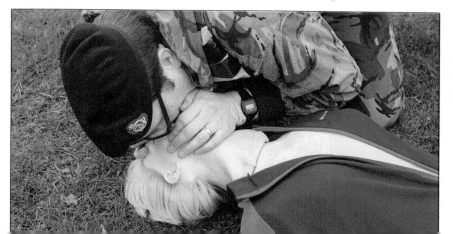

The best way to get a casualty breathing again is to use the Exhaled Air Resuscitation (EAR) method. This is best learned on the Resusca Anne type of dummy: do not practise on another person.

Is he asleep?

First, make sure that the casualty is indeed not breathing. This may seem obvious, but there have been cases of people trying to resuscitate someone who is simply asleep. The result is a nasty surprise for both. Look carefully at the casualty:

1 Is he/she unconscious?
2 Can you wake him up?
3 If not, is his chest moving?

Do not spend too long making up your mind; every moment is vital. Follow the procedure shown here, and make sure the casualty's chest is rising each time you blow. If it isn't, you are not doing it correctly.

Pinch his nose

Another common mistake is to forget to keep the casualty's nose closed. If you do not, all the air you are blowing into his mouth will simply come out through his nose.

If EAR is still not working, check that his airway is still clear and that his neck is extended properly.

Don't be squeamish

The most difficult part of EAR is getting started. The casualty may have other injuries; there may be blood and vomit in and around his mouth. He may even be dead. But apart from a quick wipe around his mouth there is no time to be lost: without prompt EAR, the casualty will die.

When the heart stops

If a casualty has stopped breathing, his heart may have stopped too. When you first examine the casualty, check his pulse by feeling the side of his windpipe: you should be able to feel the carotid artery at work. This is the best place to check, as a weak pulse is difficult to detect at the wrist.

Combining EAR and ECC

If someone's heart has stopped beating, their breathing will soon cease and you will have to carry out artificial respiration as well as cardiac massage. Ideally, two people should treat the casualty: one doing EAR and the other ECC. However, you might have to do both on your own until help arrives. If you do, then use 15 compressions of the heart to two expansions of the chest. Remember to keep the airway clear.

WARNING

You must never practise External Cardiac Compression on a real person because it is very dangerous. Never start or continue to give cardiac massage to a casualty whose heart is beating, no matter how faintly.

Below: Push down with the weight of your body, pushing the casualty's breastbone towards his spine. Lift your hand to allow the chest to recoil. Repeat 60 times per minute, checking the pulse every fifth push.

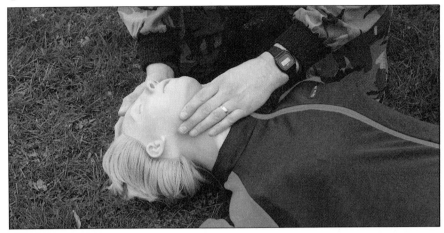

Check the casualty's pulse at his carotid artery, and if there is no pulse commence EEC. NEVER perform ECC on someone whose heart is still beating.

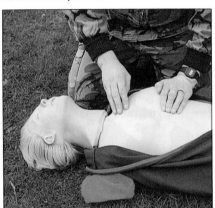

Position the casualty as for EAR: neck extended and airway clear. Now find the lower end of the sternum (breastbone).

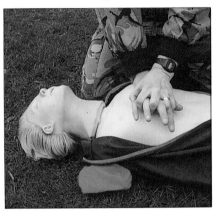

Place your hands like this: three fingers' width up, with the heel of your lower hand on the sternum.

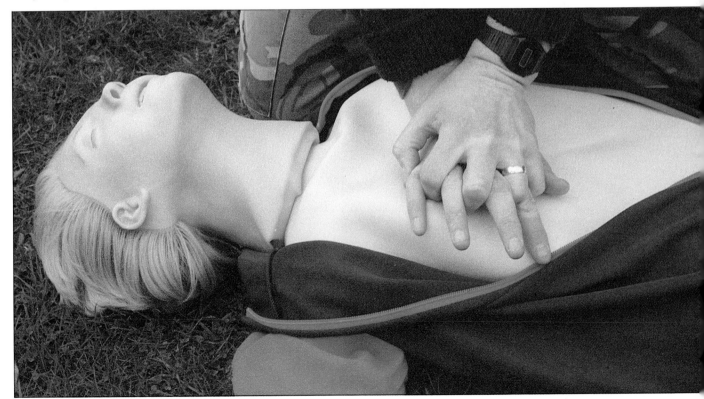

Go for it with the Galil

When the Israeli army came into being it was armed with a ragbag of rifles collected from all over the world, and supplying them all with the correct ammunition must have been a quartermaster's nightmare. In the 1950s some order was imposed, the wartime relics were discarded, and the FN FAL in 7.62-mm calibre became the standard, backed up with the heavy-barrel version as the squad automatic weapon.

During the Six Day War of 1967 Israel reached the conclusion that the FN FAL was too cumbersome and that the 7.62-mm cartridge was too powerful for the type of warfare the desert produced. At that time the US Army in Vietnam was beginning to use the M16 rifle and the 5.56-mm cartridge. A number of other 5.56-mm designs had appeared, and so the decision was taken to develop a new rifle based on the 5.56-mm cartridge.

After a period of discussion and

The Galil is another successful weapon produced by Israeli Military Industries. Closely based on the Soviet Kalashnikov design, it is manufactured in several different versions, but all are distinguished by their reliability in the toughest conditions.

The ARM is designed to fill the roles of sub-machine gun, assault rifle and light machine gun: for close-quarter fighting you can use it with the stock folded in an emergency, but will be lucky to hit anything.

The 7.62-mm version of the Galil has been developed into this sniping rifle which (in capable hands) will group its shots within a 30-cm diameter circle at 600 metres. A Nimrod 6×40 sight is supplied as standard.

assessment of various proposals, a series of tests was carried out on a selection of weapons. The M16, the Heckler & Koch HK 33, the Stoner 63 (an American design), the Soviet Kalashnikov, a rifle designed by Lieutenant-Colonel Uziel Gal (the designer of the Uzi sub-machine gun), and another designed by Israel Galil were all put through strenuous trials.

Field testing

Most of the firing was carried out in the desert, in simulated active service conditions, and much importance was attached to reliability and functioning under the most adverse conditions. None of the rifles tested was considered to be perfect, but the design submitted by Galil came closest to what the army wanted. It was selected for further development and was eventually approved for service in 1972.

Not to put too fine a point on it, the Galil is basically an improved Kalashnikov, though some critics claim that it was copied from the Finnish Valmet and that the first 1,000 rifles were built with receivers bought from Finland – which amounts to the same thing.

However you choose to look at it, the mechanism is just the same; a top-mounted gas cylinder containing a piston attached to the bolt carrier, inside which is a rotating bolt, locked and unlocked by a cam on the bolt working in a curved cam path in the carrier.

American inspiration

The firing mechanism is much the same as that in the American Garand, which has been the inspiration for many designers. This uses a hammer with two bents and a trigger unit with two sears. In single-shot mode, pulling the trigger releases the hammer to

Unlike some folding stocks, the Galil's butt is just as stable as a fixed butt. The rifle was originally developed as a 5.56-mm calibre weapon but the demand for a good 7.62-mm rifle was such that IMI soon offered an enlarged Galil, chambered for 7.62-mm NATO.

When the Americans first encountered the AK-47 in Vietnam they soon learned that a 20-round magazine is simply too small. The AK has a 30-round magazine and the Galil goes one better, offering a 35-round magazine as standard. They also produce a 50-round magazine, primarily intended for when the Galil is being used as a light machine-gun.

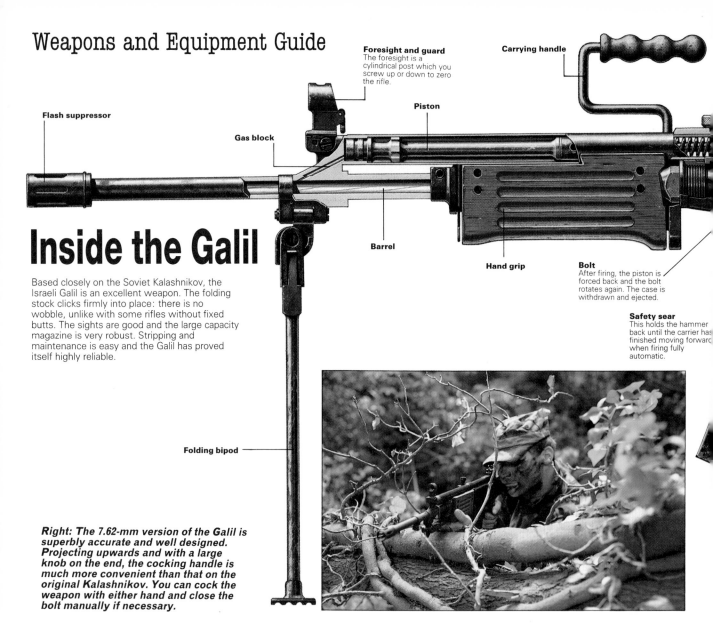

Foresight and guard
The foresight is a cylindrical post which you screw up or down to zero the rifle.

Carrying handle

Piston

Gas block

Flash suppressor

Inside the Galil

Based closely on the Soviet Kalashnikov, the Israeli Galil is an excellent weapon. The folding stock clicks firmly into place: there is no wobble, unlike with some rifles without fixed butts. The sights are good and the large capacity magazine is very robust. Stripping and maintenance is easy and the Galil has proved itself highly reliable.

Barrel

Hand grip

Bolt
After firing, the piston is forced back and the bolt rotates again. The case is withdrawn and ejected.

Safety sear
This holds the hammer back until the carrier has finished moving forward when firing fully automatic.

Folding bipod

Right: The 7.62-mm version of the Galil is superbly accurate and well designed. Projecting upwards and with a large knob on the end, the cocking handle is much more convenient than that on the original Kalashnikov. You can cock the weapon with either hand and close the bolt manually if necessary.

strike the firing pin. As the bolt carrier comes back, under the pressure of the gas piston, it rotates the hammer back until it is caught on the second bent and auxiliary sear.

The bolt then goes back and reloads, but since the firer is still holding the trigger pressed, nothing happens.

When the firer releases the trigger and re-pulls it, the auxiliary sear is withdrawn and the hammer goes down to fire the next shot.

Automatic firing

On automatic fire the hammer is rocked back as before and is held by the safety sear. The bolt closes, and as it does so the safety sear is released so that the hammer goes down and fires once more, the firer having kept the trigger pressed all the time. This continues as long as the trigger is held down; as soon as it is released, the hammer is caught once more.

Stripping the Galil

The Galil in 7.62 mm or 5.56 mm field-strips for normal daily cleaning in exactly the same way as the Kalashnikov, to which it bears more than a passing resemblance.

1 Check the safety, remove the magazine, release the safety and cock the weapon to eyeball the chamber. Release it, but do not fire off the action.

2 Press in on the take-down catch on the rear of the receiver and remove the receiver cover by lifting up and to the rear.

3 Pull the recoil spring assembly backwards out of the bolt carrier, and remove it.

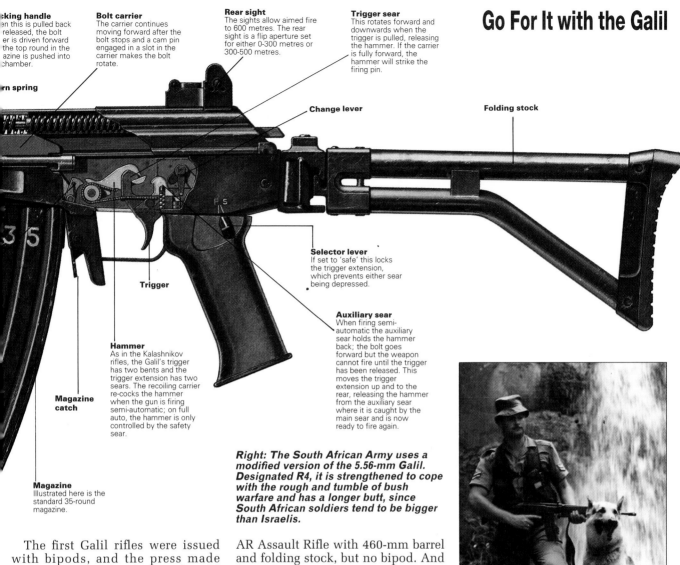

cking handle
en this is pulled back
released, the bolt
er is driven forward
the top round in the
azine is pushed into
chamber.

rn spring

Bolt carrier
The carrier continues
moving forward after the
bolt stops and a cam pin
engaged in a slot in the
carrier makes the bolt
rotate.

Rear sight
The sights allow aimed fire
to 600 metres. The rear
sight is a flip aperture set
for either 0-300 metres or
300-500 metres.

Trigger sear
This rotates forward and
downwards when the
trigger is pulled, releasing
the hammer. If the carrier
is fully forward, the
hammer will strike the
firing pin.

Change lever

Folding stock

Selector lever
If set to 'safe' this locks
the trigger extension,
which prevents either sear
being depressed.

Auxiliary sear
When firing semi-
automatic the auxiliary
sear holds the hammer
back; the bolt goes
forward but the weapon
cannot fire until the trigger
has been released. This
moves the trigger
extension up and to the
rear, releasing the hammer
from the auxiliary sear
where it is caught by the
main sear and is now
ready to fire again.

Trigger

Hammer
As in the Kalashnikov
rifles, the Galil's trigger
has two bents and the
trigger extension has two
sears. The recoiling carrier
re-cocks the hammer
when the gun is firing
semi-automatic; on full
auto, the hammer is only
controlled by the safety
sear.

**Magazine
catch**

Magazine
Illustrated here is the
standard 35-round
magazine.

*Right: The South African Army uses a
modified version of the 5.56-mm Galil.
Designated R4, it is strengthened to cope
with the rough and tumble of bush
warfare and has a longer butt, since
South African soldiers tend to be bigger
than Israelis.*

The first Galil rifles were issued with bipods, and the press made much of the fact that the bipod could be used for cutting barbed wire and for opening beer bottles, though in truth there was nothing new about either of those ideas. Very soon, though, three distinct patterns of Galil appeared, to be used as appropriate by different types of troops.

The standard rifle is the ARM. This has a 460-mm barrel, a bipod, and a folding tubular stock. Next comes the AR Assault Rifle with 460-mm barrel and folding stock, but no bipod. And for airborne and commando troops there is the SAR (Short Assault Rifle) with 332-mm barrel, folding stock and no bipod.

Magazine capacity

The standard magazine contains 32 rounds, but a 50-round magazine may be used with the ARM in the light machine-gun role. The muzzle is shaped into a flash hider and is of the

4 Slide the bolt and bolt carrier to the rear of the receiver and then lift it out.

5 Rotate the bolt to separate it from the bolt carrier. The bolt carrier is fixed to the piston rod, where most of the carbon is deposited during firing.

6 The gas piston tube slides off the body backwards, allowing you to clean out the gas block.

A South African signaller armed with an R4 rifle. This version of the Galil has been tested in bush warfare conditions.

standard 22-mm external diameter, so that rifle grenades may be fired from the AR and ARM models.

Once the Galil had been issued to the Israel Defence Force, the manufacturers (Israel Military Industries) began looking at the export market. It was sold to Bolivia, Guatemala and Nicaragua, and the South African Army adopted a slightly modified version as its 'R4'.

It appeared that there were armies still looking for a good 7.62-mm rifle, and so the design was now modified to 7.62-mm NATO calibre in the same three versions, the ARM and AR with 535-mm barrels and the SAR with a 400-mm barrel. So far as we are aware,

only small numbers of these have been sold and they are not in service in any quantity.

The last design

The last of the Galil designs appeared in the early 1980s as the 'Galil Sniper'. The 7.62-mm SAR had been tried as a sniping rifle, but the Israeli Army felt that it was not good enough and made some suggestions for improvement which IMI followed up. The result was a recognisably Galil weapon but with a much heavier barrel, a muzzle brake to reduce recoil, a more solid (though still folding) butt, a bipod attached to the receiver, and a sturdy mount for an

Battlefield Evaluation: comparing

Galil

If you consider the Galil as a weapons system – 5.56-mm, 7.62-mm; short and long barrels plus specialist sniper rifles – the only manufacturer who competes is Heckler & Koch. The H&K series of rifles also covers a wide range, all stemming from the 7.62-mm G3 rifle. The other weapons considered here come close but are not as comprehensive a system.

Specification:
(5.56-mm ARM)
Cartridge: 5.56mm
Weight: 4.91kg
Length: 979mm
Cyclic rate of fire: 650 rounds per minute
Magazine: 35- or 50-round box

Assessment
Reliability	★★★★
Accuracy	★★★★
Age	★★
Worldwide users	★★

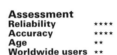

The Galil weapons system has proved outstandingly successful in combat, from the Middle East to Nicaragua.

Heckler & Koch

All H&K rifles work on the same roller-delayed blowback system and have a general resemblance. The G41 is their latest 5.56-mm weapon, available in long and short barrelled versions with fixed or folding butt. It also has a three-round burst facility which the Galil lacks. In 7.62-mm there is the standard G3 or the very advanced G8. For sniping there is the PSG-1 with heavy barrel, adjustable stock and sensitive trigger.

Specification: (G41)
Cartridge: 5.56mm×45
Weight: 4.1kg
Length: 997mm
Cyclic rate of fire: 850 rounds per minute
Magazine: 30-round box

Assessment
Reliability	★★★★
Accuracy	★★★★
Age	★★
Worldwide users	★

Like the Galil, Heckler & Koch produce a range of rifles based on the same operating mechanism.

Valmet M76

Valmet of Finland make an improved Kalashnikov in 5.56 and 7.62-mm calibres, and there is probably very little to choose between these and the Galils. There is also a heavy-barrel version, the M78, for use as a machine-gun. However, for sniping they offer the M86, a superbly accurate conventional bolt-action single-shot weapon.

Specification: (M76)
Cartridge: 7.62mm× 39 or 5.56mm×45
Weight: 4.51kg (7.62-mm model with 30-round mag)
Length: 914mm
Cyclic rate of fire: 650 rounds per minute
Magazine: 15-, 20- or 30-round box

Assessment
Reliability	★★★★
Accuracy	★★★
Age	★★★★
Worldwide users	★

Built to survive the toughest conditions, Valmet rifles are Finnish developments of the Kalashnikov.

optical sight. The positioning of the bipod gives a stable weapon without placing any stress on the barrel, and it is close enough so that the firer can reach out and adjust it without undue movement.

The sight bracket allows the telescope sight to be mounted and dismounted rapidly without affecting the zero of the weapon. There is also a two-stage trigger which gives an almost hair-trigger release, and there is no provision for automatic fire. The barrel is 508-mm long, and there is a special 20-shot magazine. The Galil Sniper has been in use with the Israeli forces for some years, but has not yet been exported in any numbers.

A South African cavalry patrol armed with R4 rifles: some government units used horses during the Rhodesian war, and cavalry may continue to serve in Southern Africa for some time to come.

the Galil with its rivals

Fabrique National

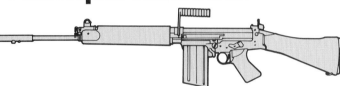

The FN company produces 5.56-mm and 7.62-mm assault rifles but they are of entirely different design. The 7.62-mm model is the well-known FAL, modified for British service as the L1A1 SLR; this uses a tipping bolt to secure the breech. The 5.56-mm FNC uses a rotating bolt. For sniping purposes, FN offer a third rifle, the Model 30-11 bolt action, which uses a Mauser-type bolt and a heavy barrel.

Specification: (FN FAL)
Cartridge: 7.62 mm×51
Weight: 5 kg
Length: 1143 mm
Cyclic rate of fire: 650-700 rounds per minute
Magazine: 20-round box

Assessment
Reliability ★★★
Accuracy ★★★
Age ★★★★★
Worldwide users ★★★★★

FN FALs capable of automatic fire in the hands of Caribbean troops during the liberation of Grenada.

CETME

This Spanish design team uses the same sort of roller-locked delayed blowback system as does Heckler & Koch – indeed, they developed it first – and make the C3 in 7.62-mm and the model L in 5.56-mm. Both are very good weapons and both have outfitted the Spanish forces, the Model L gradually replacing the C3. The C-75 sniping rifle is a bolt action based on the Mauser design.

Specification:
(Model L)
Cartridge: 5.56 mm×45 NATO
Weight: 3.4 kg unloaded
Length: 925 mm
Cyclic rate of fire: 600-750 rounds per minute
Magazine: 12- or 30-round box

Assessment
Reliability ★★★
Accuracy ★★★
Age ★★
Worldwide users ★

Like the H & K rifles derived from it, the CETME design has been used for both 7.62 mm and 5.56 mm calibre.

Kalashnikov

The Kalashnikov system ranges from the 7.62-mm AKM now largely replaced by the 5.45-mm AK-74 and a sub-machine gun version issued to Special Forces and some airborne units. The sniping rifle is the Dragunov, which is the same basic mechanism but carries a heavier, longer barrel and an optical sight. None of these weapons approach their Western equivalents when it comes to accuracy, but for robustness under tough conditions they are hard to beat.

Specification: (AK-74)
Cartridge: 5.45 mm
Weight: 3.6 kg unloaded
Length: 930 mm
Cyclic rate of fire: 650 rounds per minute
Magazine: 30-round box

Assessment
Reliability ★★★★
Accuracy ★★★
Age ★★
Worldwide users ★★

An original 1950s AK-47: subsequent Kalashnikov designs have used the same basic method of operation.

Firing the MP5

Sub-machine gun design tends towards two extremes: the cheap and cheerful, like the Sten gun and the Soviet wartime designs – crude weapons which can kill you just as well as more expensive guns – or the complex and costly, like the Swiss MP41. But there is a middle area where quality and cost sometimes come together to produce something which gives the best of both worlds, and one of the most outstanding examples of this is the Heckler & Koch MP5 design.

The Heckler & Koch company was formed in the 1950s and began making a blowback pistol. It was then tapped by the Bundeswehr to take a rifle then being offered to the German army and develop it into a more practical weapon. The rifle was the G3, and it incorporated a roller-delay breech mechanism which had first been put together in an experimental Mauser rifle in 1945.

Post war development

The Mauser men went to Spain after the war and worked on their design for CETME, the Spanish 'think tank', and through a Dutch intermediary offered the rifle to Germany. After H&K had worked on it the rifle was adopted, and has since been employed by innumerable armies around the world.

Heckler & Koch then took the same basic breech mechanism and applied it to a variety of other rifle designs, then to some machine-guns, and final-ly to a sub-machine gun. This was something of a gamble, because very few sub-machine guns with a compli-cated mechanism had ever prospered. But the H&K weapon has one supreme advantage over most other sub-machine guns: it fires from a closed breech.

Most SMGs are prepared for firing by pulling back the breech block and holding it there; when ready, the firer presses the trigger and the block is driven forward by a spring to chamber the round, fire it, and be blown back by the force of the explosion acting on the empty case.

Closed breech

The H&K design, on the other hand, cocks the gun by pulling back the breech block and cocking a hammer, then allowing the block to go forward, load a cartridge and close the breech without firing. When the trigger is pressed the hammer falls, strikes a firing pin, and the gun fires.

What this means in practice is that when you pull the trigger of an aver-age sub-machine gun there is a per-ceptible shift in weight and balance as the heavy bolt flies forward and slams into the chamber, and accurate firing under these circumstances is pot luck. With the H&K design the minimal

Below: The MP5 is aimed: it has the same type of aperture and post sights as fitted to H&K rifles. The magazine is the small, 15-round version, which makes for a very compact gun when you fit it to an MP5 with collapsible stock.

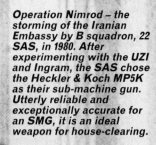

Operation Nimrod – the storming of the Iranian Embassy by B squadron, 22 SAS, in 1980. After experimenting with the UZI and Ingram, the SAS chose the Heckler & Koch MP5K as their sub-machine gun. Utterly reliable and exceptionally accurate for an SMG, it is an ideal weapon for house-clearing.

Above: Firing an aimed burst from the shoulder, the MP5 is highly accurate. Because it fires from a closed breech your aim is not spoiled by a moving bolt altering the balance of the gun at the moment you fire.

movement of the hammer doesn't affect the balance or the aim, and thus you have a far higher chance of hitting the target with the first shot.

The MP5 uses a pressed-steel body with plastic butt and pistol grip and a plastic handguard surrounding the barrel. There is a housing above the barrel into which the cocking handle, return spring and part of the bolt fits, and the rest of the bolt hangs down behind the barrel.

Two-part bolt

The bolt is divided into two parts, a light front section and a heavier rear section, and the two are connected by a pair of rollers and the firing pin. As the breech closes, so the forepart of the bolt thrusts a cartridge from the box magazine into the chamber and stops. The rear part of the bolt, riding along behind, squeezes the two rollers, which are between the two parts of the bolt, outwards into recesses in the receiver. Unless these rollers are fully out and fitting their recesses, there is insufficient space between them to permit the firing pin to pass, so that it is impossible to fire the weapon unless the bolt has functioned properly.

When the trigger is pressed, a hammer is released to strike the firing pin and fire the cartridge. The explosion pressure then forces the cartridge backwards and tries to force the breech block back as well. The front part moves very slightly, but is then

stopped by the rollers, which interfere with the rearward movement.

To obtain any more movement the forepart of the bolt has to drive the rollers out of their recess, and this recess is carefully angled so that in order for the rollers to move they must push back the rear part of the bolt, which is heavy, at a mechanical disadvantage.

Operating cycle

This slows down the rearward movement and allows the bullet to leave the barrel and the pressure inside the chamber to drop to a safe level before the rollers come free and the entire bolt unit begins to move back, extracting and ejecting the empty case. The bolt then moves back freely, cocking the hammer and loading a return spring; it stops, then begins moving forward again to repeat the cycle.

The assault team is ready to storm a building in a Counter Revolutionary Warfare exercise. The lead member of the team carries a Heckler & Koch MP5K, which was specifically introduced for police and anti-terrorist action.

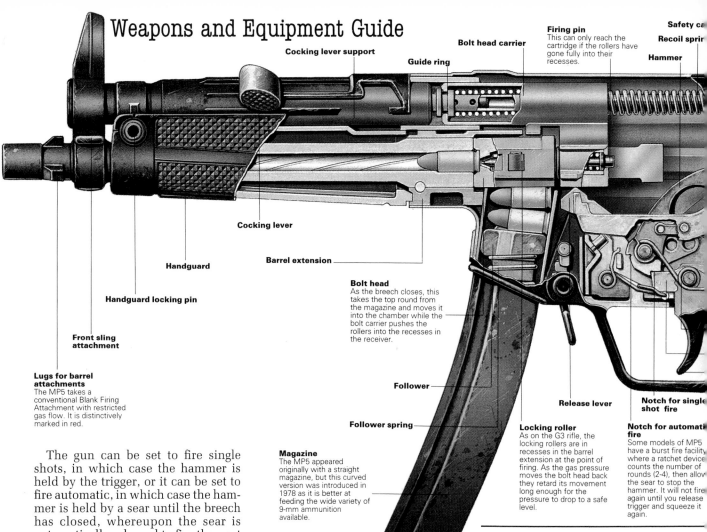

Cocking lever support

Cocking lever

Guide ring

Bolt head carrier

Firing pin
This can only reach the cartridge if the rollers have gone fully into their recesses.

Safety ca

Recoil sprir

Hammer

Handguard

Barrel extension

Handguard locking pin

Bolt head
As the breech closes, this takes the top round from the magazine and moves it into the chamber while the bolt carrier pushes the rollers into the recesses in the receiver.

Front sling attachment

Follower

Release lever

Notch for single shot fire

Lugs for barrel attachments
The MP5 takes a conventional Blank Firing Attachment with restricted gas flow. It is distinctively marked in red.

Follower spring

Locking roller
As on the G3 rifle, the locking rollers are in recesses in the barrel extension at the point of firing. As the gas pressure moves the bolt head back they retard its movement long enough for the pressure to drop to a safe level.

Notch for automati fire
Some models of MP5 have a burst fire facility where a ratchet device counts the number of rounds (2-4), then allow the sear to stop the hammer. It will not fire again until you release trigger and squeeze it again.

Magazine
The MP5 appeared originally with a straight magazine, but this curved version was introduced in 1978 as it is better at feeding the wide variety of 9-mm ammunition available.

The gun can be set to fire single shots, in which case the hammer is held by the trigger, or it can be set to fire automatic, in which case the hammer is held by a sear until the breech has closed, whereupon the sear is automatically released to fire the next round. In automatic mode the MP5 fires at about 800 rpm.

At one time the MP5 was fitted with a straight magazine, and it was possible to have a firing mechanism which allowed controlled three-round bursts as well as automatic fire. This option has now been dropped, and the magazine is now curved; models holding 15 or 30 rounds are available.

There are a number of variant models of the MP5. The current

Captured Iranians aboard USS Guadalcanal are escorted to helicopters by US Special Forces personnel armed with a mixture of M16s and H&K MP5A3s.

models are the MP5A2 with fixed butt and the MP5A3 with sliding metal butt. The MP5SD is the silenced version; this has the barrel enclosed in a silencing shroud and there are some 30 holes in the barrel which allow the propelling gas to be leaked into the silencer, so reducing the noise made by the exit of gases from the muzzle. This also, of course, cuts down the velocity of the bullet to some degree, but nobody ever got a silenced weapon without sacrificing some performance.

There are three versions of the SD: the MP5SD1 has a cap on the rear of the receiver and no butt; the SD2 has a fixed butt, and the SD3 has the sliding metal butt. There were also three other models, the 4.5 and 6 which were the same as the 1, 2 and 3 but had the three-round burst option; these are no longer manufactured.

The final model of the MP5 family is the MP5K, designed for use by police and anti-terrorist squads who wanted the most compact weapon possible. It uses exactly the same mechanism but

Stripping the MP5

1 Remove the magazine and pull back the cocking handle. Look in the breech to check that there is no round in the chamber.

4 The pistol grip can now hinge down.

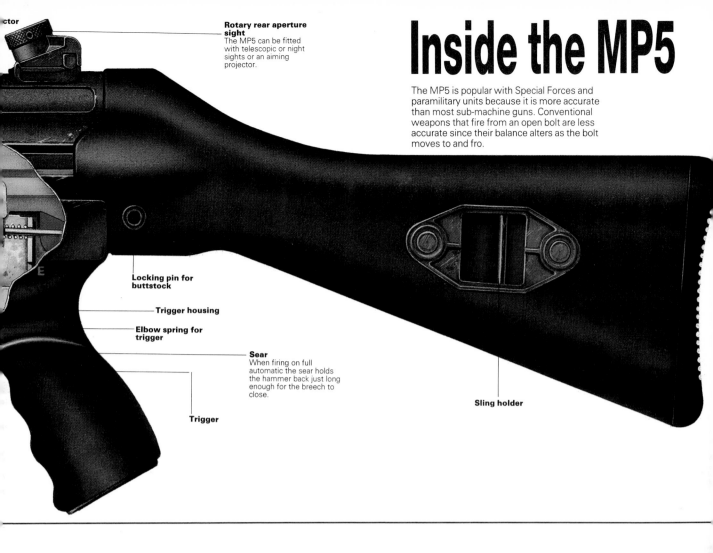

ctor

Rotary rear aperture sight
The MP5 can be fitted with telescopic or night sights or an aiming projector.

Inside the MP5

The MP5 is popular with Special Forces and paramilitary units because it is more accurate than most sub-machine guns. Conventional weapons that fire from an open bolt are less accurate since their balance alters as the bolt moves to and fro.

Locking pin for buttstock

Trigger housing

Elbow spring for trigger

Sear
When firing on full automatic the sear holds the hammer back just long enough for the breech to close.

Trigger

Sling holder

2 Pull out the locking pin behind the pistol grip.

3 Remove the butt.

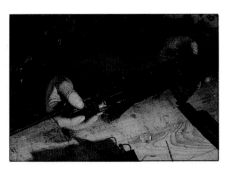

5 Pull back the cocking lever to permit the bolt and return spring to come out of the rear of the receiver.

6 By turning the bolt head through 90° it can be taken out of the bolt body and the firing pin can be removed.

7 The field strip of the MP5 completed: further dismantling is not necessary for routine maintenance. Most SMGs with complex mechanisms have proved to be failures, but the MP5 is an exception.

is much shorter, has a forward hand grip and no butt of any sort, and uses a 15-shot magazine as standard. The 30-shot magazine can be used, but this rather destroys the compactness of the design. The MP5K can be carried underneath a jacket or fitted into a briefcase and fired by a trigger contained in the handle, for inconspicuous carriage by bodyguards.

A list of the forces using the MP5 and its variants, if one could be acquired, would be a long and in-

The MP5 SD is the silenced version of the sub-machine gun. The barrel has 30 3-mm diameter holes and a silencer which reduces the muzzle velocity to subsonic level.

Battlefield Evaluation: comparing

Heckler & Koch MP5

The H&K MP5 has established itself as one of the best SMGs available today, and its widespread use by Special Forces and paramilitary units testifies to its effectiveness and reliability. Very few SMGs fit exactly into the slot occupied by the MP5, since few employ a comparable mechanism: the weapons examined here are the closest competitors.

Specification:
Cartridge: 9-mm Parabellum
Weight: 3 kg
Length: 58 cm
Cyclic rate of fire: 800 rounds per minute
Magazine: 15- or 30-round box

Assessment
Reliability   *****
Accuracy   *****
Age   ***
Worldwide users   ****

Extremely accurate and reliable, the MP5 is an ideal weapon for anti-terrorist action.

Spectre

This new Italian SMG is unique in employing a 'double-action' mechanism, allowing you to carry it loaded and cocked but safe; to fire you simply pull the trigger. The gun is loaded by pulling back the cocking handle and releasing it, which allows the bolt to go forward, chamber a round and close the breech. The hammer is held by the trigger but can be released by a de-cocking lever and allowed to slide forward under control. When you pull the trigger, the hammer is cocked and released just like on a double action revolver. It is therefore ideal for security or counter-terrorist action.

Specification:
Cartridge: 9-mm Parabellum
Weight: 2.9 kg empty
Length: 58 cm (stock extended)
Cyclic rate of fire: 900 rounds per minute
Magazine: 30- or 50-round box

Assessment
Reliability   *****
Accuracy   *****
Age   **
Worldwide users   *

Spectre breaks new ground in SMG design and is a good choice for CRW units and paramilitary duties.

Skorpion

This small Czech SMG, now made in Yugoslavia, was designed as a personal defence weapon for tank crew but its size makes it a favourite terrorist weapon. Firing 7.65-mm (.32 auto), its small bolt produces a high rate of fire, so a 'rate reducer' is fitted into the pistol grip. As the bolt goes back it drives down a weight against a spring; the bolt is locked at the rear until the weight bounces back up the grip and releases it. You can imagine what the bouncing up and down does to your accuracy.

Specification:
Cartridge: 7.65 mm (.32ACP)
Weight: 2 kg loaded
Length: 27 cm (stock retracted)
Cyclic rate of fire: 840 rounds per minute
Magazine: 10- or 20-round box

Assessment
Reliability   ***
Accuracy   **
Age   ****
Worldwide users   **

The Skorpion is a favourite terrorist weapon, easily concealed and lethal at close range.

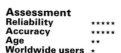

teresting one. It is in extensive use by military and police forces throughout the world and is now being manufactured under licence in Greece, Portugal and Turkey.

It received a great deal of publicity in Britain after being seen in the hands of the SAS during the Iranian Embassy affair, and is carried by police at the major British airports. Its utter reliability and superlative accuracy give it an edge, for certain applications, over most other contenders.

*Part of the **SAS** team storming the Iranian Embassy. They are entering the rear of the building at ground level, slipping quietly into the library, MP5A2s at the ready.*

the MP5 with its rivals

Steyr AUG 9 Para

This type of weapon may pose a threat to the conventional SMG in the near future. It is, in effect, an assault rifle in 9-mm calibre. The Steyr AUG is a well-known 5.56-mm assault rifle; the '9 Para' model is a conversion which can be done very simply because of the AUG rifle's modular construction. The stock and receiver remain the same, but the barrel is changed and the bolt mechanism is replaced by an unlocked blowback bolt unit. The resulting weapon fires from a closed bolt and its 407-mm barrel gives remarkable accuracy out to 200 metres.

Specification:
Cartridge: 9-mm Parabellum
Weight: 3.8 kg loaded
Length: 69 cm
Cyclic rate of fire: unknown
Magazine: 30-round box

Assessment
Reliability	*****
Accuracy	*****
Age	*
Worldwide users	*

*The **AUG** is the Steyr rifle in 9-mm calibre, almost identical to this **AUG** short-barrelled carbine.*

UZI

The UZI is to some extent the SMG by which others are judged. It has been in the field a long time and has a remarkable record of reliability in combat, but it is an older generation of weapon and is absolutely conventional, firing from an open bolt. Compact, even in its standard form, the Mini-UZI and Micro-UZI versions are small enough to fit comfortably under your clothing. The only problem with these smaller versions is their recoil when firing the 9-mm cartridge, and they are difficult to keep on target without a great deal of practice.

Specification:
Cartridge: 9-mm Parabellum
Weight: 4 kg
Length: (stock folded) 47 cm
Cyclic rate of fire: 600 rounds per minute
Magazine: 25-, 32-, or 40-round box

Assessment
Reliability	*****
Accuracy	****
Age	*****
Worldwide users	*****

*The **UZI** has an impressive combat record but represents a very different approach to **SMG** design.*

Beretta PM12

Robust and accurate, the Beretta PM12 is not just a very good-looking SMG; it is a very useful weapon. The receiver has grooves inside running its full length, which help to keep the mechanism working even if sand or mud enters the gun. The Beretta is a very steady weapon with little muzzle climb on full auto and impressive accuracy when firing single shots.

Specification:
Cartridge: 9-mm Parabellum
Weight: 3.8 kg
Length: 42 cm (stock folded)
Cyclic rate of fire: 550 rounds per minute
Magazine: 20-, 32- or 40-round box

Assessment
Reliability	*****
Accuracy	*****
Age	****
Worldwide users	***

*The **Beretta Model 12** is accurate, very controllable and an excellent **SMG** all round.*

Bounding into battle with the BTR-60

A BTR-60 comes ashore with a PT-76 light tank in the background. Despite its weaknesses as an amphibious assault vehicle, the BTR-60 remains the standard APC of Soviet Naval Infantry.

Not every important military vehicle is a multi-million dollar sophisticated fighting machine. The BTR-60 series of eight-wheeled armoured personnel carrier is a brutally simple combat vehicle with no frills and few concessions to crew comfort. An old design which broke no new technical ground and introduced no tactical innovation, the BTR-60 remains one of the most significant Warsaw Pact military vehicles and will stay in general use to the end of the century. The reasons for its success shed interesting light on Soviet military thinking and the tactical use of their infantry fighting vehicles.

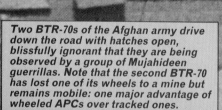

Two BTR-70s of the Afghan army drive down the road with hatches open, blissfully ignorant that they are being observed by a group of Mujahideen guerrillas. Note that the second BTR-70 has lost one of its wheels to a mine but remains mobile: one major advantage of wheeled APCs over tracked ones.

The BTR-60 was adopted by the Soviet army in about 1960, first appearing in public during the 1961 November Parade. Meanwhile, the US Army was re-equipping itself with the tracked, box-like M113 APC in its effort to give infantry similar mobility to tanks.

High mobility

It seems logical to provide infantry with a tracked vehicle like a tank and the next Soviet APC to be developed, the BMP, was the first in the series of increasingly powerful tracked combat vehicles which today includes the British MCV-80 Warrior and American M3 Bradley. However, a wheeled vehicle offers many advantages and multi-wheeled APCs have remained very popular despite, or perhaps because of, the rise of the cannon and missile-armed Infantry Combat Vehicle.

A wheeled APC is considerably cheaper to build and operate than a tracked vehicle. It will last much longer as the wear and tear on its main automotive parts is far less, and it requires only a fraction of the fuel demanded by a track-layer. The BTR-60 is half the weight of the new generation of IFVs, which allows it to use bridges that would collapse under an M2 Bradley. And although a powerful tracked vehicle can travel over terrain that would bog down a wheeled APC, the US Army estimates that in Europe this denies a BTR access to no more than 10 per cent of the terrain. If, like the Soviets, you need an awesome number of APCs,

the economic argument triumphs.

Before the BTR-60 the Soviet infantryman rode into action on the BTR-152, little more than an armoured 6×6 truck. Many walked. As the Soviets reorganised their army in the expectation of combat under nuclear conditions, they raced to increase the mobility of their army and introduced the BTR-60 to carry half a platoon.

Series production

After several years of intensive production at the factories in Gorky, enough BTR-60s had been churned out to provide one per section, and most Motor Rifle Divisions continue to rely heavily on the BTR-60 and its descendants.

Weighing a modest 10 tonnes, the

BTR-60's woodlouse-on-wheels appearance stems from the need to be amphibious and large enough to carry up to 16 fully-equipped troops. On all models of the BTR-60, the driver and commander sit at the front of the hull with the troop compartment behind them and the engine at the rear.

The two water-cooled six-cylinder petrol-driven engines are not the safest powerplant to put in an APC – petrol invariably burns if the vehicle is penetrated – but the Soviets have continued to rely on it for nearly 30 years. In any case, the BTR-60 is not built to take punishment; its armour is nowhere more than 9-mm thick and, in many places, barely bullet-proof. However, it is a sobering thought that few APCs, even the Bradley or the Warrior, can withstand much more than small-arms fire, so the Soviet approach is not unreasonable.

On the first production model, the BTR-60P, the crew compartment was open-topped and a pair of pintle-mounted 7.62-mm machine-guns were mounted to fire over the sides near the front. Another machine-gun, usually a 7.62-mm PKB or SGMB, was fitted to fire forward, operated by the commander. Sometimes a heavier DShKM 12.7-mm weapon was substituted.

BTR-60PB

The open-topped BTR-60P had obvious disadvantages as an APC, and it was rapidly superseded by the BTR-60PB, which remains the most numerous BTR-60 model in service in the 1980s. The crew compartment was roofed over and a turret fitted, armed with the monstrous KPV 14.5-mm heavy machine-gun, able to chew up most light AFVs that the BTR-60 might encounter. A co-axial 7.62-mm gun was added for good measure.

Close-up of the driver's station on a BTR-60 knocked out by US forces during the liberation of Grenada. The driver's hatch is supposed to be closed when in action and has an integral vision device.

The Soviet belief that a future conflict would probably involve the use of nuclear weapons made an NBC system a priority and the BTR-60, for all its apparent age and simplicity, had a more effective system than many contemporary NATO APCs. With respectable armament and high battlefield mobility, the BTR-60 is an effective APC well able to meet the demands of mechanised warfare. Its speed is sufficient to out-distance Main Battle Tanks travelling cross-country providing the going is reasonable, and its amphibious capability enables it to tackle water obstacles with ease.

Unusually for a Soviet combat vehicle, it is an enjoyable vehicle to drive; it is fast, responsive, and able to bounce across country in splendid style. A US Army officer has been quoted as calling the BTR-60 that he had tested as 'the ultimate RV' (Recreational Vehicle).

Disadvantages

If the BTR-60 is fun for the driver, it can be less so for the infantrymen in the troop compartment. There is one small hatch in each side, and your main means of exit are two not over-large hatches in the roof. To scramble out of these top hatches and drop over the side of a moving BTR-60PB is an exciting and potentially risky business. Deploying under fire can be disastrous.

Even the drivers' enthusiasm for the vehicle was dented when the Soviets invaded Afghanistan, because the Afghan resistance discovered an Achilles heel: the wheel wells are only armoured with mild steel, and a well-aimed burst from an AK directed at the front tyre would shred the rubber, penetrate the hull and hit the driver in the head.

The BTR-60PB remains the standard APC of Soviet Naval Infantry and is used to land troops direct from the sea. However, it is hardly the equal

More non-tactical movement by Afghan government soldiers in a BTR-70. One man on the back of the vehicle wears the bush hat commonly worn by Soviet soldiers in Afghanistan during the summer. The BTR-70 was intended as a replacement for the BTR-60, but was not a success, and the BTR-80 has now been introduced.

Inside the BTR-60

of a dedicated amphibious assault vehicle such as the LVTP-7 of the US Marines. The BTR-60's slow speed in the water rules out using it in an opposed landing, as the assault troops would be sitting in the water under fire for an unacceptably long time. It cannot cope with a heavy swell and can only land through 0.6 metres of surf, whereas the Marine Corps vehicle can hit the beach in over three metres of surf.

BTR-70

For all its crudity and apparent drawbacks, the BTR-60PB had been in service for nearly 20 years before an improved model was detected by the West. In 1980 a new version was observed in the November Parade and has received the Western designation of BTR-70. The new vehicle has better protection at its front, especially over the front wheel area, and has three closely-spaced firing ports in the centre of the hull. The side door is smaller, in the lower part of the hull between the middle wheels, and the troops sit on a bench running along the centreline of the vehicle.

The BTR-70 retains the same turret as the BTR-60PB and the same armament, but is driven by new and more-powerful engines. Some BTR-70s seen in Afghanistan have had AGS-17 30-mm automatic grenade-launchers fitted on the roof behind the driver's station, in addition to the turret armament.

Disappointment

According to US sources, the BTR-70 did not live up to expectations and production was terminated in the early 1980s while BTR-60PBs were still being manufactured for export. The BTR-70 did not improve the most significant weaknesses of the design; the engines, although more powerful, are still petrol driven and the hatches are still badly designed for an infantryman going somewhere in a hurry.

A tough and soldier-proof vehicle, the BTR-60PB continued in production into the early 1980s despite the introduction of the revolutionary BMP Infantry Fighting Vehicles. The Soviets continue to place high value on wheeled APCs, which are far cheaper than tracked combat vehicles. This is a BTR-60PB used throughout Africa, the Middle East and the Warsaw Pact except Poland and Czechoslovakia.

Ventilator fla

Screw hydrojet

Water port

Exhaust

Air intakes

Tunnel for water propulsion

Radiators

Tyres
Foam-filled, they are resistant to small-arms fire although a sustained burst from a GPMG or shell fragments from mortar or artillery fire will deflate them. On the other hand, like British Saladins in Cyprus they can trundle about on several flats and survive mine damage which would immobilise a tracked APC.

Troop compartment

Weapons port
On the BTR-60 you can only fire directly to the sides from within the vehicle, which leaves a blind spot over the forward arc where the turret guns cannot depress far enough to engage and the weapons ports do not cover. This is rectified on the BTR-80, in which the weapons ports are angled to allow forward fire.

In the last few years the Soviet army has been replacing elderly BTR-60s with a third version, the BTR-80, in which a single V-8 diesel developing 260 hp is substituted for the pair of petrol engines. This produces a slight increase in speed and better fuel economy as well as reducing the risk of fire.

The BTR-80 has a similar turret to preceding models, but the 14.5-mm machine-gun can be elevated to +60° as opposed to the 30° of the earlier APCs. Whether this is because of difficulty in engaging guerrillas shooting down from high mountain crags in Afghanistan is open to speculation, but it certainly improves the anti-aircraft capability of a Motor Rifle unit. The Soviets have always trained to fire absolutely everything available at hostile aircraft, and high-angle 14.5-mm machine-guns will be particularly useful. The Western practice of having forward-firing smoke dischargers has been adopted on the latest generation of Soviet Main Battle

A BTR-60PB obtained by the United States: this is the most prolific of BTR-60 variants and a great improvement over the original open-topped version. Note the trim vane under the bow, which is erected for amphibious operations, and the numerous handles along the hull side for troops to climb up.

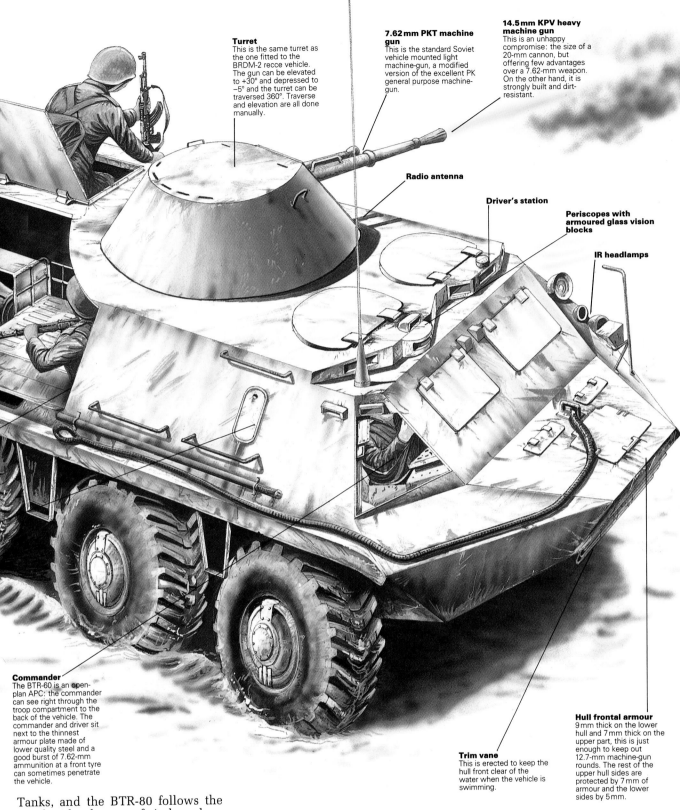

Turret
This is the same turret as the one fitted to the BRDM-2 recce vehicle. The gun can be elevated to +30° and depressed to −5° and the turret can be traversed 360°. Traverse and elevation are all done manually.

7.62mm PKT machine gun
This is the standard Soviet vehicle mounted light machine-gun, a modified version of the excellent PK general purpose machine-gun.

14.5mm KPV heavy machine gun
This is an unhappy compromise: the size of a 20-mm cannon, but offering few advantages over a 7.62-mm weapon. On the other hand, it is strongly built and dirt-resistant.

Radio antenna

Driver's station

Periscopes with armoured glass vision blocks

IR headlamps

Commander
The BTR-60 is an open-plan APC: the commander can see right through the troop compartment to the back of the vehicle. The commander and driver sit next to the thinnest armour plate made of lower quality steel and a good burst of 7.62-mm ammunition at a front tyre can sometimes penetrate the vehicle.

Trim vane
This is erected to keep the hull front clear of the water when the vehicle is swimming.

Hull frontal armour
9mm thick on the lower hull and 7mm thick on the upper part, this is just enough to keep out 12.7-mm machine-gun rounds. The rest of the upper hull sides are protected by 7mm of armour and the lower sides by 5mm.

Tanks, and the BTR-80 follows the trend with a battery of six launchers mounted on the back of the turret.

You can get in and out of a BTR-80 much more easily than of the BTR-60, as a two-part side hatch is fitted. The lower part forms a step while the upper section opens outwards: the result is a far more sensible arrangement that allows you to dismount quickly without being so exposed to

BTR-60s have seen action all over the world in the last 25 years. However, they are best suited to low-intensity operations: BTR-60s counter-attacking US forces on Grenada were destroyed by an AC-130 gunship.

enemy fire. Three firing ports are provided in the side but they are at an oblique angle, enabling you to shoot into the forward arc of the vehicle rather than perpendicular to the hull side. This removes a potentially dangerous area of dead ground close to the APC's front which the turret-mounted machine-guns could not depress sufficiently to cover.

The revolutionary BMP series of Infantry Fighting Vehicles equip the infantry battalions in tank regiments

The BTR-70 can be distinguished from the BTR-60 by the gap between the second and third wheels, which houses a small door. The front of the vehicle is more heavily armoured.

Battlefield Evaluation: comparing

BTR-60

Still in widespread service with the Warsaw Pact and encountered throughout Africa and the Middle East, the BTR-60 is easy to maintain and has a superb cross-country performance. Its successors, the BTR-70 and BTR-80, are still no match for an IFV like the Warrior, but they are only a fraction of the cost to build and operate. The Soviets continue to place great value on the wheeled APC, introducing new models alongside the BMP and BMP-2.

Specification:
Crew: 2+14
Combat weight: 10.3 tonnes
Road speed: 80 km/h
Power-to-weight ratio: 18 hp/tonne
Length: 7.5 m
Height: 2 m
Armament: 1×14.5-mm and 1×7.62-mm machine-gun

Assessment
Firepower ★
Mobility ★★★★★
Age ★★★★★
Worldwide users ★★★★★

The BTR-60's amphibious performance is too weak to allow an opposed landing.

BTR-152

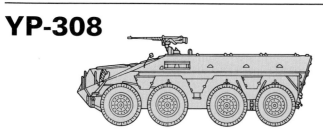

No longer in front-line service with the USSR, the BTR-152 still trundles about with reserve formations throughout the Warsaw Pact and is widely used in North Africa and the Middle East. The chassis is based on that of a ZIL 6×6 truck and the vehicle is little more advanced than a bullet-proof lorry. The BTR-152 has no amphibious capability, which the Soviet army soon regarded as a serious disadvantage and which became a major reason for the introduction of the BTR-60 and BTR-50.

Specification:
Crew: 2+17
Combat weight: 9 tonnes
Road speed: 75 km/h
Power-to-weight ratio: 12 hp/tonne
Length: 6.83 m
Height: 2 m
Armament: 1×7.62-mm machine-gun

Assessment
Firepower ★
Mobility ★
Age ★★★★★
Worldwide users ★★★★

The BTR-60 was introduced to replace the BTR-152s, seen here used by the US Army for training purposes.

YP-308

A contemporary of the BTR-60, the YP-308 was adopted by the Dutch army in the early 1960s and is now being replaced by the FMC Advanced Infantry Fighting Vehicle. The YP-308 is inferior to the BTR-60 in several key areas: it is not amphibious, has no NBC system, and the machine-gunner has no protection. On the other hand its diesel engine is less of a fire hazard, and access to the troop compartment is better.

Specification:
Crew: 2+10
Combat weight: 12 tonnes
Road speed: 80 km/h
Power-to-weight ratio: 13.75 hp/tonne
Length: 6.2 m
Height: 2.4 m
Armament: 1×7.62-mm machine-gun

Assessment
Firepower ★★
Mobility ★★★
Age ★★★★★
Worldwide users ★

The Dutch YP-308 appeared shortly after the BTR-60 and is now being replaced by the FMC AIFV.

and form the cutting edge of the Motor Rifle Divisions, but have not replaced the BTR-60. Despite the failure of the BTR-70, the Soviets have persevered with a replacement wheeled APC which will presumably take the place of the BTR-60. Like the original, it may not be fancy but it is far cheaper than a tracked combat vehicle, has a good performance, adequate armament and fair protection, following the Soviet tradition of simple but effective combat vehicles.

A brewed-up BTR-70 in Afghanistan: note the small door open on the hull side between the second and third wheels and the cover of the waterjet on the hull rear, which is partially ajar.

the BTR-60 with its rivals

AT105 Saxon

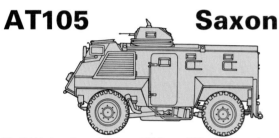

The British Army has ordered over 500 Saxon APCs, and may order over 1000 of these modern wheeled APCs for a wide variety of tasks ranging from personnel carriers to Internal Security, recce, command post and recovery vehicles. UK-based infantry battalions earmarked to reinforce BAOR in wartime will use the Saxon as their standard APC

Specification:
Crew: 2+10
Combat weight: 11.6 tonnes
Road speed: 96km/h
Power-to-weight ratio: 14 hp/tonne
Length: 5.1m
Height: 2.48m
Armament: 1×7.62-mm machine-gun

Assessment
Firepower   *
Mobility   ****
Age   **
Worldwide users ***

The AT105 Saxon is a second-line APC used in the British Army for units not scheduled to receive MCV-80.

VAB

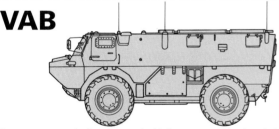

Twenty years ago the French army decided to use a combination of wheeled and tracked APCs. The powerful but expensive AMX-10P MICV is supplemented by large numbers of VABs in 4×4 configuration. It is a very successful APC; the French army has ordered over 4,000, and it has been sold widely in Africa and the Middle East. It is fully amphibious and can be modified for many different combat roles.

Specification:
Crew: 2+10
Combat weight: 13 tonnes
Road speed: 92km/h
Power-to-weight ratio: 17 hp/tonne
Length: 5.98m
Height: 2.49m
Armament: 1×7.62-mm or 1×20-mm cannon or 1×90-mm gun or 1×120-mm mortar or HOT or MILAN anti-tank missile launchers

Assessment
Firepower   **
Mobility   *****
Age   **
Worldwide users ***

The VAB serves in an astonishing variety of roles. This model is equipped with a 20-mm cannon.

Transportpanzer

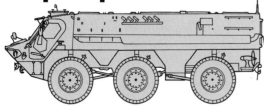

The Transportpanzer is part of a series of wheeled combat vehicles developed for the West German army during the 1960s. In German service it serves as a supply carrier, ambulance, and command and communications vehicle, and is also used for NBC recce and combat engineering. It is amphibious and has a full NBC system; armament can be varied according to its particular task.

Specification:
Crew: 2+10
Combat weight: 17 tonnes
Road speed: 105km/h
Power-to-weight ratio: 18.8 hp/tonne
Length: 6.76m
Height: 2.3m
Armament: 1×7.62-mm machine-gun or 1×20-mm cannon

Assessment
Firepower   ***
Mobility   *****
Age   ***
Worldwide users **

The West German army uses the Transportpanzer in a multitude of combat and support roles.

Downed in the Desert

When you find yourself stranded in the Sahara, you'll have to make up your mind whether to stay where you are, or try to move on. It's a decision governed by circumstances. If you've been travelling by aircraft, the pilot will have filed a flight plan. Similarly, employees of oil and water prospecting companies and similar organisations file a route plan with an estimated time of arrival. In the event of your non-arrival, a search and rescue plan will be put into action. Clearly, the best course here will be to remain with the aircraft or vehicle until help arrives.

The problems arise if you're stranded while engaged on military activities for real, or on expeditions to more remote regions where the chances of rescue are slim at best. In one region in the Sahara, some 43 people died in a single year. These are recorded deaths; the actual figure may be higher.

In temperate or tropical zones the environment is relatively kind. The survivor is rarely far from materials, water, foodstuffs and people to assist in an emergency. The desert militates against this, and the decision to stay or move is much more difficult to make.

You must consider your assets, equipment, physical state, mental state, navigational skills and equipment, water, food, location, and the size of your party. Then you must weigh these against the distances involved, the terrain, your chances of rescue, weather, temperatures etc.

How far can you go?

By walking slowly and resting for 10 minutes every hour, a man in good physical condition can cover between 12 and 18 miles per day if he has sufficient food and water. If you plan on walking during the day, you may get 10 miles to one gallon of water. At night, you could possibly double that distance, since you will dehydrate less. If lack of water is a problem, then moving at night is more sensible. The disadvantages are that you may bypass water supplies and habitation.

Choose the easiest route. Go round obstacles, not over or through them. Zig-zag to prevent over-exertion when climbing. Visibility for a man six feet tall is limited to between five and six miles when standing on a flat plain.

Sand mats are essential even for Saharan 'roads'. If you are not in convoy, getting bogged in could land you in serious trouble. It is well worth fitting a power winch and carrying sand anchors so you can pull yourself out.

One of the most difficult problems in the featureless desert is maintaining direction. An error of a few mils in the bearing can mean you miss an oasis by hundreds of metres. A theodolite, if you have one, is a real asset.

Vital skills

To improve your chances of survival in the desert, learn and practise these basic skills before going abroad. The average soldier will be familiar with most of the following, but may find one or two techniques that aren't in the Army manual.
- Map reading
- Compasses, bearings, back bearings and variations
- Direction-finding using sun and stars
- Direction-finding using shadow stick methods
- Water location, extraction and purification
- Heat and its effects and how to avoid them
- First Aid
- Signals – ground to ground and ground to air

Signals

You should carry a copy of the Morse alphabet in your survival kit. And try to memorise the May Day signal, along with the newer Pan Pan signal. This is a lower priority signal recognised by all international maritime and aircraft crews.

May Day — — · — — · — — — · ·
Pan Pan · — — · · — — ·

Include in your kit a set of ground to air signals as follows:

Require doctor – serious injury
Need medical supplies
Unable to proceed
All is well
Do not understand
Am moving in this direction
Indicate direction to proceed
Need compass and map
No
Yes

Survival on the coast

Your choices of direction are reduced to two, since you can be certain that people will be living along the coast somewhere. You can also be sure of finding fresh water, where rivers discharge into the sea. (The term "fresh" means non-salt rather than drinkable.) All water will be heavily polluted, so take all precautions to make sure the water you drink is sterile.

You can also get "fresh" water by digging several beach wells. Dig the holes a safe distance above the high-water mark, and deep enough to permit water to collect in the bottom. Skim off and use only the top layer of water – this will be less salty than the denser sea water below it.

The sea shore also has plenty of things living or growing on it that you can eat.

Signalling

Set signal fires in threes, arranged in a large triangle with sides approximately 20 metres long. In daylight, the glare from the ground and from the air reduces the visibility of wood fires as wood in the desert is so dry that it is smokeless. Add oil, rubber, plastic or green plants, if available, to generate smoke.

You can also use mirrors for signalling over long distances in the desert.

Set ground signals, too. These last a

Above: The Sahara is not camper van country, as these tourists have just found out. It is probably one of the most testing environments imaginable, and four-wheel drive is an essential, not an optional extra.

long time and need little or no maintenance. Lay out a large SOS in stone, preferably of contrasting colour to the ground, but at least large enough to cast a well-defined shadow.

There is an international system of ground to air signals which is worth carrying in your survival kit.

Fluorescent signal panels are a useful addition to your kit. Learn the international distress signal and the

You must prepare for every eventuality; that includes having to walk out. This is the way to do it, with a 5-gallon water jerrycan mounted on an aluminium rucksack frame with shelter kit and sleeping bag fixed on top.

Signalling with an air signal panel

Air panels are light, easy to carry and should be carried by at least two members of a patrol. The US issue VS-17 signalling panel is a simple plastic sheet which is violet on one side and orange on the other. Use the orange side to initially attract the pilot's attention. Flashing the panel will make it easier to spot. You can then use the panel to pass information as shown. You can use any reasonable substitute for the panel, e.g. liferaft sails, bright-coloured rain jackets etc.

on land and at sea
OK to land (arrow shows landing direction)

on land and at sea
need medical attention

on land and at sea
do not attempt landing

on land and at sea
need first aid supplies

on land and at sea
plane is flyable; need tools

on land
need gas and oil; plane is flyable

on land
need warm clothing

at sea
need exposure suit or clothing indicated

on land
indicate direction of nearest civilisation

at sea
indicate direction of rescue craft

have abandoned plane
on land
walking in this direction

at sea
drifting

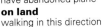

on land and at sea
need food and water

on land
should we wait for rescue plane?

at sea
notify rescue agency of my position

at sea
need equipment as indicated (signals follow)

on land
need quinine or atabrine

at sea
need sun cover

Survival

Sandstorms
Sandstorms or sand-laden winds occur regularly in most desert areas: for example, the "Siestan" or desert wind of Afghanistan and Iran can blow up constantly for up to 120 days. Wind speeds in the storm could reach 70 to 80 miles per hour by early afternoon. Major dust storms can be expected at least once a week. When confronted with this you should take cover and mark its direction of travel. These storms will effect radio transmissions.

Navigation
On the coast your choice of direction is limited to two, as you can be sure that people will live along the coast somewhere. You must be totally familiar with all the survival navigation techniques and practise them before you need them.

"Voluntary dehydration"
If you only drink when you are thirsty you will generally drink only 65 per cent of your daily requirement. To avoid this voluntary dehydration, at temperatures below 100 degrees drink one pint of water every hour; at temperatures above 100°, drink two pints every hour.

Signal fires
Signal fires should be set in the shape of a triangle with the fires 20 metres apart. These are useless in the intense sunlight of the day unless you use plant material or oil to produce smoke. Smothering a fire with leaves tends to produce white smoke, and oil produces black smoke: make sure you produce a colour that contrasts with the background.

Night marching
Although you will conserve water by moving at night, visibility on moonless nig[ht] is extremely poor and travelling is very hazardou[s]. Dangers include getting l[ost], falling into ravines, and missing water sources. Conversely, moonlit night[s] are usually crystal clear, w[ith] none of the problems associated with daylight moves; winds die down a[nd] haze and glare disappear, [so] you will be able to see lig[hts] at great distance, and nois[e] will carry further.

Air panel
Make sure you carry a fluorescent air panel in your survival kit. These can be used not just to draw the initial attention of a rescue aircraft but also to pass messages to the aircraft.

Estimating distance
If you do decide to send o[ff] a party to find help, remember that things always seem closer than they are in the desert by a factor of three. So a rough guide is that anything that looks one mile away is in reality three miles away.

Food discipline
If water is scarce, do not eat. Water is required for digestion of food and you need that water for cooling.

Limit movement
Any essential work should be done at night. During the day, get under cover, put something between you and the hot ground, and stay there.

Insects
Lice, mites, wasps and flies, which are drawn to man as a source of water and food, are extremely unpleasant and may carry disease. Old buildings, ruins and caves are favourite habitats for spiders, lice, scorpions, centipedes and other wildlife that can make life unbearable. Take extra care when sheltering in these areas. Always wear gloves and do not sit down or lie down without visually inspecting the area first.

Conserving sweat
In this situation you are not going to have unlimited amounts of water, so if you cannot control the amount of water you take in you have to control the amount your body loses. This means complete body coverage. Roll your sleeves down and cover your head and neck. This will protect your body from the hot sand-laden winds and the direct rays of the sun. Your clothes will absorb your sweat and keep it against your skin so you gain the full cooling effect.

Stay in the shade
If you stay in the shade quietly, fully clothed, not talking, keeping your mouth closed and breathing through your nose, your water requirement will drop dramatically and consequently you will last a lot longer.

Above and right: Klaus Boehme and Hans Hauser sip the last of their water from a plastic canteen shortly before their death in the Egyptian Siwa desert after their vehicles broke down. Later they partially buried themselves in the sand to reduce the dehydration. These photographs were found in the camera of Mrs Boehme with the bodies. All five people in the party died of thirst.

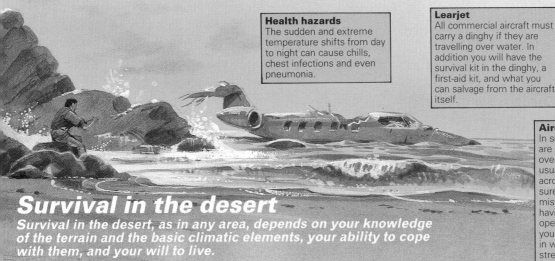

Health hazards
The sudden and extreme temperature shifts from day to night can cause chills, chest infections and even pneumonia.

Learjet
All commercial aircraft must carry a dinghy if they are travelling over water. In addition you will have the survival kit in the dinghy, a first-aid kit, and what you can salvage from the aircraft itself.

Aircraft wrecks
In some desert areas there are many aircraft wrecks left over from the war. These usually have 'wreck' painted across the wings. Make sure your aircraft cannot be mistaken for a wreck by having at least one signal operative at any one time. If you can, put out a large SOS in wreckage or stones on a stretch of the beach.

Survival in the desert

Survival in the desert, as in any area, depends on your knowledge of the terrain and the basic climatic elements, your ability to cope with them, and your will to live.

reply. The distress signal is six flashes of light, six blasts of a whistle or six waves of a signal flag, followed by a break of one minute before repeating the sequence. The response is three long blasts, waves, or flashes.

Direction finding

With a map and compass you should be able to establish your position. Without these, you will have to improvise.

To find north, first establish south by pointing the hour hand of your watch towards the sun. Then find the mid point between the hour hand and the 12 o'clock position. The line from the centre of your watch to here points south.

Remember that if you are in a desert in the southern hemisphere, the procedure is slightly different. Point the 12 o'clock position towards the sun and bisect the angle between the 12 o'clock position and the hour hand. This points to the north.

A digital watch can be used for the same task, despite opinions to the contrary. Either mark with a grease pencil or imagine the conventional watch face and hands showing the time, overlaid on the digital face. Then continue as above.

Remember that the sun rises in the east and sets in the west to within a few degrees. Remember also that in the northern hemisphere, the sun is to the south of us, and in the southern hemisphere the sun passes to the north of us.

The east-west line

Place a one-metre stick vertically into the ground and mark the tip of its shadow with a stick or stone. After 15 minutes, place another stick or stone to mark the tip of the new shadow position. The straight line that joins these two points indicates, roughly, east/west.

The north-south line

Put a stick into the ground in the morning, and mark the tip of its shadow on the ground. Using a piece of string anchored to the base stick,

draw an arc. The arc must be the same length as the shadow line you've just drawn. In the afternoon, when the tip of the shadow touches the drawn arc once more, draw a further line from the arc to the base stick. Bisect the angle formed between the two lines and the resulting line will indicate north/south.

Night moves

If you move at night, you will need to be able to recognise certain star constellations that either point the way north or point to the North Star (sometimes known as the Pole Star). The constellations to learn are the Plough, Orion, and Cassiopea. They appear at different times during the night throughout the year and revolve, so they may well appear upside down when compared with conventional star charts.

You must learn your constellations before you set out on any journey that involves the risk of being stranded. And *practise* all your survival skills before you need to use them.

Taking on the Saharan Challenge

Few vehicles even remotely suited to conditions in the Sahara will be likely to survive the desert "off the peg" — so they will need plenty of specialist work before your expedition starts. Your choice of vehicle will be governed by many factors – including the size of your party, distances involved, fuel and water loads, spares, foodstuffs, personal and expedition equipment. The conversion of Land Rovers and other popular vehicles is well documented elsewhere. This article will cover the modification of ex-German Army Mercedes Unimog 404S vehicles.

We bought four vehicles to take on a 10-week, 26-person expedition across Algeria, through Niger and into Chad. Two vehicles were delivered on a lowloader, a third was towed in by the fourth – the only one that was a runner. The first task was to strip the vehicles down completely to the bare chassis. Then we cleaned and repainted them, made welding repairs to the bodywork, rebuilt the floors in the cargo space and began work on the engines, brakes, electrics, wiring and special modifications.

Starting with the brakes, we replaced all the corroded pipe runs with steel pipe, which we made up to fit, and ordered replacement rubber hoses from Germany. Anticipating very heavy loads and steep hills, we decided to fit servo units to the brake system to boost the brakes. Regrettably, these units did not arrive until two days before we were due to depart. We did not fit them, but later wished we'd had time to do so.

Long-range 'mog

The Unimog is fitted with two 10-gallon fuel tanks with a change-over tap as standard. On three of the vehicles we fitted 25-gallon Bedford replacement tanks as the originals were holed. Using the change-over tap, we fitted an additional 25-gallon tank to all vehicles giving a 45- or 50-gallon capacity in tanks. We carried extra fuel in heavy-duty five-gallon plastic jerry cans as used by the army.

We had arranged to have fuel delivered to a remote outstation in the desert in 44-gallon drums and knew we would need a hand-operated pump. Therefore, we had a manual Zwicky pump, mounted on the front wing of one vehicle, that delivered about 10 gallons per minute. We regularly used this, too, for transferring fuel from tank to tank when dirty fuel clogged the taps and circumstances prevented us from clearing the lines on the roadside during the day.

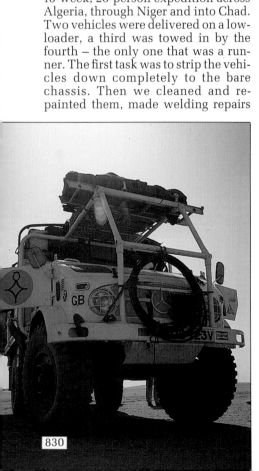

A good cross-country vehicle must have good ground clearance and a sump plate to protect the engine from damage. This vehicle has been modified by the addition of Bedford truck wheels and tyres, which means an extra four inches' ground clearance over the standard model.

Higher and higher

For economy, we bought Bedford tyres, complete with rims, from a breaker's yard, at less than 25 per cent of the cost of new Unimog tyres. An engineer machined out the wheel centres and welded in new ones, drilled to fit the Unimog wheel studs. These larger wheels increased the already plentiful ground clearance by a further 4 inches. We mounted the spare wheel, displaced by fitting the extra fuel tank on the underside of the body, in a specially constructed frame welded to the aftermost part of the vehicle chassis.

As we expected the vehicles to run in high summer temperatures (in fact they went as high as 136°F) we had some collars machined for the oil filters. These diverted the oil through modified Land Rover oil coolers mounted on the front bumpers in pro-

Vehicle checklist

Long before you buy a vehicle for travel in the Sahara, you must consider where your journey will take you, what you are going for, when, for how long, and how many people will go. All these considerations will affect the type and amount of equipment to be carried, the stores, water, the number and size of vehicles and spares required. Once you've worked out your cargo, route and fuel needs, you can acquire the vehicle to suit.

Once you have the vehicle, consider how big an overhaul it needs before departure. A new vehicle should be run in the UK for some while, to allow rust to stiffen nuts and bolts – the Sahara will quickly find all weaknesses and shake bolts loose. Work towards bringing the vehicle up to a standard of reliability somewhat higher than you might accept in the UK. Renew everything that is suspect. Allow yourself a generous safety margin of time as things can, and do, go wrong, even at this early stage.

Now consider your Sahara specification – the extra in-line fuel filters, the oil cooler, large radiator, heavy duty suspension (it is a fact of life that all vehicles departing for the Sahara are grossly overloaded), the fire extinguishers, roof rack, the spares lists, the specialist tools, compasses, the jacks and sand channelling.

Next consider your personnel, their water requirements, food, cookers, camping gear and stowage for personal equipment. Have you, in fact, got enough space for all those jerry cans and food boxes, scientific gear, medical and photographic equipment, or do you need a different vehicle?

Do your homework before you start!

The trans-Saharan leg of Operation Raleigh provided one of the most gruelling tests of equipment, vehicle and crew endurance. The vehicles chosen for the job were ex-West German army Unimog trucks, which were completely rebuilt in England with some interesting modifications.

tective frames. On the expedition, one of the vehicles still persisted in running hot, so the mechanics fabricated a second radiator from the heater unit of a wrecked Peugeot car, and plumbed it into the vehicle's cooling system.

Each vehicle crew specialised in a particular field, specifically photography, mechanics, science and medicine. Each vehicle was carrying specialist equipment in addition to basic equipment. The photographic vehicle carried a number of batteries, which continually required charging.

The roll cage was specifically designed to bear the weight of the engine block so the engine could be lifted out for repairs on a block and tackle. The cab has also been rebuilt to lift out easily after first removing the cage. The cage is then replaced to carry out the work.

Unimogs are fitted with 24-volt systems, but the photographic equipment demanded 12 volts. We therefore had a small transformer made and fitted, so that we could either charge batteries on the move or use the equipment direct from the vehicle batteries. For the scientific equipment, which required mains voltage, we carried a small Suzuki generator.

Double insurance

At the rear of each open cab, we installed a rectangular-shaped, diagonally braced roll cage. This was further strengthened by two "bull horns" attached to the cage and extending forward over the cab and down onto the front bumper bar. This cage would have provided some protection in the event of an accident, but like everything else on the expedition, had a second use.

It was also intended, and in two instances was used, to let us carry out major engine works in the field. We had to change two clutches, and did so by removing the front part of the cage, removing the cab and then replacing the cage. We suspended a winch from a movable bar across the top of the "horns" and attached it to the engine. We then unbolted the

Above: On the expedition the team had to replace two clutches. When selecting a vehicle, the ease with which major repairs can be done is an important consideration. Another problem is spares: it is no good taking a mechanically superior vehicle if you end up having to carry all your own spares, which may have to include a spare axle.

Left: Rocky desert gives suspension systems a real pounding, and conventional springs are not ideal. Although damage like this will not disable the vehicle, it will make for a difficult trip with the possibility of further vibration damage if it is not repaired.

Below: You must have excellent all-round visibility, which tends to exclude anything with a long bonnet where you cannot see what you are driving into. The Unimog's height and driving position mean that the driver can see exactly where he is putting the wheels.

engine from the bell housing and rolled it forward on the bar. Re-assembly was the reverse of this procedure. We might have had to abandon the two vehicles and perhaps abort the expedition had we not had this facility.

The roll cage also provided a framework for the lightweight luggage racks we had made up and bolted on. We carried our light personal "immediate use" equipment in these, which also provided us with shade from the very hot sun.

Our expedition ran two types of Unimog: a cargo vehicle with two seats in the front, and a crew cab version that had two seats in front with a four-person bench seat immediately behind. On the cargo vehicles, we installed two old London bus seats facing inward aft of two 44-gallon water drums, which were mounted on a retaining plinth and lashed to the bulkhead. The crew cabs also carried two 44-gallon water drums in the cargo space.

Distributed between the four vehicles were two Tirfor winches, two steel winch cables, two heavy-duty tow chains and a specially fabricated heavy tow bar. We used the tow bar ourselves once, while the chains were used on several occasions to extricate other travellers in trouble.

The Unimog proved the ideal tool for our requirements. Given the time and money, we would choose them above all else for a similar expedition.

Above: Old faithful. The safari Land Rover may not be as capable as some vehicles cross-country, but it is such a popular vehicle and has been around so long that spares are obtainable virtually anywhere, even in Africa. Note the extra fuel and water containers fitted externally.

Below: The layout of the Operation Raleigh cargo vehicles. Meticulous preparation and careful packing is not just a question of convenience, but one of survival in such hostile terrain. Incorrect packing means equipment gets damaged and the vehicle becomes unbalanced.

Above: The Zwicky pump fitted to the wing of the vehicle for pumping fuel from drums too heavy to lift into the vehicle fuel tanks. In the event of a power failure you could also find this useful for pumping fuel from underground tanks. It may be slow but it works.

Interpreting Air Photographs

Air photographs can provide you with a wealth of information. Special Forces' personnel have to be as proficient with an aerial picture as with a map. At first it may seem rather daunting, but it is a useful skill to learn and enables you to make maximum use of the latest intelligence. Air photographs give you up-to-date information and allow you to study the ground in great detail, making them a handy aid to patrol planning. Unlike a map, a photograph may reveal the location of enemy positions.

Air photographs have a number of disadvantages which you must bear in

The RF-101 Voodoo was used in Vietnam for photo recce missions.

Right: Having overcome the defenders, including the Special Forces A team, Viet Cong guerillas burn the village.

mind. They are not gridded, and contour lines are difficult to make out. They carry no scale and in mountainous country the scale can actually vary from point to point. But if you combine them with a map, your

ability to plan ahead is doubled.

Air photographs may be taken at a vertical or oblique angle. Vertical views are generally more valuable because more can be gleaned from them; like maps, they are an accurate plan of the ground with no hidden areas. Since the scale is constant over the whole print, it is simple to understand. Oblique photographs, on the other hand, are complementary, presenting a familiar, panoramic view, but the scale varies from the foreground to the background and you cannot see into the dead ground behind hills, hedges, buildings and other vertical obstacles.

This is the North Korean airfield of Uiju after a visit from the USAF during the Korean war. Ten Superfortresses dropped airburst and demolition bombs, which have cratered the main runway. This was followed up by a low-level strafing attack by F-86 Sabres, which destroyed several MiGs that can be seen in the revetments.

Setting the photo to the map

There are two methods of roughly orientating a photo to the map:

1 Orientate by using time (obtained from the titling strip) and shadows on the picture to find approximate north.
2 Find prominent objects on both map and photograph. When you have found them, mark the grid reference on the picture.

Finding the scale

There are two ways to scale the photograph:

1 Representative fraction method

This uses the information on the titling strip. The scale of the photo is FL divided by 12H: FL is the focal length of the lens, and H is the height of the aircraft in feet. For example, if the focal length of the camera is 8 inches and the aircraft was flying at 12,000 ft, the scale of the map is equal to 8 divided by 12×12,000. The result is 1/18,000.

2 Air photo/map comparison method

This is simpler: select two prominent points on the map 1,000 metres apart. Locate the same points on the photograph. Using a piece of paper, mark off the distance between these two points on the photo. Put that distance on to the border of your photo, divide into 10 subdivisions and you have an instant 1,000-metre scale, subdivided into 100-metre units. If you cannot find two obvious terrain features 1,000 metres apart, use any convenient points. For example, if they are 1,800 metres apart, divide the distance into 18 sections of 100 metres.

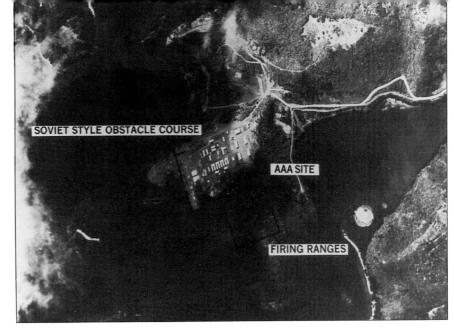

Even high-level photo recce can reveal some very interesting information to the trained eye. Analysis of this photograph of Calivigny barracks on Egmont in Grenada in 1983 gave an indication of the size and strength of the garrison and what weapon systems they were using.

The titling strip

Air photographs carry a titling strip added to the picture during processing to help you understand what you are looking at. The format is now standardised throughout NATO and consists of the following items:

1 Print number
This is shown on the left.

2 Camera position
When a camera is installed to produce true vertical pictures it is known as a 'single vertical camera'. The following letters identify the camera position:
V When used singly, this refers to a single vertical camera. If more than one is installed in the aircraft, they are numbered from nose to tail, e.g. V1, V2 etc. If the cameras are installed side-by-side but do not form a split pair giving overlapping pictures, they are numbered from port to starboard.
F The single letter F indicates a fan of two or more cameras. The letter is followed by two figures: the first indicates the number of cameras, the second the position of the camera within the fan. Cameras are numbered according to the area of ground photographed, e.g. in a fan of four cameras, the camera photographing the ground on the extreme left would be numbered F41. If an aircraft carries

more than one fan, they are numbered from nose to tail and this is indicated by a number appearing in front of the letter F.
S Indicates a starboard-facing oblique camera.
P Indicates a port-facing oblique camera.
N Indicates a nose-mounted oblique camera. If there is more than one, they are numbered from port to starboard, e.g. N1, N2 etc.
T Indicates a tail-mounted oblique camera.

3 Squadron number
This appears in figures only, e.g. 52 means No. 52 Squadron.

4 Service
This serves to distinguish between squadrons of the same number but belonging to different Air Forces.

5 Sortie number
Sortie numbering for a squadron starts at 1 and ends at 9,999, when it goes back to 1 again. If more than one film is exposed during a sortie, the sortie number is followed by a part number to indicate the magazine, e.g. Pt 1, Pt 2 etc.

6 Date
This is shown in the form of 28 SEP 88. If taken either side of midnight it will be shown as 28/29 SEP 88.

All the information you need to make sense of the photograph is printed on the photo. This is print number 84, taken by a single vertical camera by No. 58 Squadron of the RAF, who at the time were flying Canberra PR.Mk 9s. The sortie number was 7422 and was flown on 3 June 1966, time 0930 Zulu (GMT). The focal length of the camera was six inches and the shot was taken at 9,000ft.

7 Time
The time is given in Greenwich Mean Time (GMT), known to the armed forces as Zulu time, so it is shown with the suffix Z.

8 Focal length
The focal length is useful in establishing the scale of the photograph.

9 Security classification
Air photography has the same grading as official correspondence and is slowly downgraded as the subject matter decreases in importance.

10 Additional information
This may include geographical detail, e.g. place names. The aircraft's altitude is sometimes included but this is the mean height of the machine during the sortie, not necessarily the height at which the picture was taken.

Orientating, gridding and finding the scale

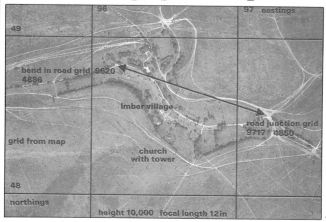

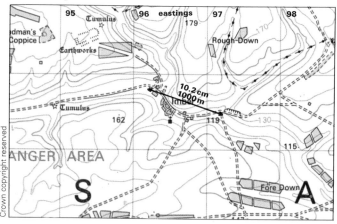

Here you have an air photograph of Imber village and the corresponding area of a 1:50000 Ordnance Survey map. You can see at a glance that the photograph is immediately more useful in terms of the amount of detail it shows. You should be able to orientate the photograph by inspection. The church is a prominent object on both (grid reference 9650 4835). Next, pick two points on the map that you can identify on

the photograph that are exactly one kilometre (two cm) apart. Thus one kilometre on the ground corresponds to 10.2 cm on the photograph, which also corresponds to 2 cm on the map. From any of the points you can identify on the photo and the map, you can plot the position of the nearest grid lines and grid the photograph so that you can use it like a map.

Plotting a north/south line on your photograph

A north/south line can be plotted using the map as reference. Select two points on the map that appear clearly on the photo, draw a line between them and measure the bearing. Draw a line through the same two points on the photo, lay off the bearing and you have a north/south line. Bearings taken on the north/south line should be accurate to within 20 mils as long as the photograph is a true vertical and the ground is not too hilly.

Gridding the photograph

This is a more difficult and lengthy task because every grid line plotted must be plotted in at least three different places and then connected up. To reduce distortion, try to select grid

lines somewhere near the centre of the picture. The sequence is as follows:
1 Select a grid line and follow it on your map. Select three prominent points on the map which the line runs through.
2 Find the same three points on the photo and join them with a continuous line. It is obviously important that the line is accurate.
3 Having plotted your first vertical line, select a horizontal line and follow the same procedure. Use a protractor to check that the lines form a right angle, otherwise you could be in big trouble.
4 Having got two grid lines on the map you can use your 1,000-metre scale to assist in drawing the rest of the grid. You must regularly compare the grid lines you are drawing with

those on the map to check that they conform.
5 Don't panic if the grid lines become inaccurate near the edge of the photo. You can expect a little distortion here.

Reading air photographs

To the uninitiated, a vertical air photograph can be very confusing. You are presented with a bird's-eye view of the world in which familiar objects can appear quite unrecognisable. However, with regular practice

Port Stanley airfield shows the results of the Vulcan bomber attack. The photo was officially credited to a Harrier although the mission was probably flown by a Canberra PR.Mk 9 based in Chile, because the Harrier cannot be equipped with a vertical camera and using the oblique camera to produce such a photograph would have been difficult.

Harrier nose camera

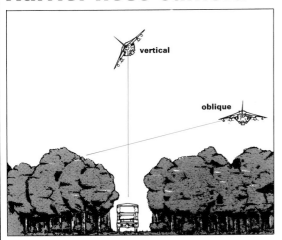

In theory, the 18-degree nose camera in the Harrier can be used to produce a vertical or an oblique photograph. Tactically the low angle obliques are more useful as you can concentrate on the target even if it is covered by the trees.

The nose camera in the Harrier is set at 18 degrees, so to sight in the camera the pilot flies at exactly 18 degrees' opposite tilt from his instruments and then looks through his canopy at the far horizon. Where that cuts his canopy, he marks a line with a Chinagraph pencil.

Then, when flying level, the line on his canopy tells him where the camera is pointing. All he has to do is make sure the line on the canopy cuts the target as he flies past.

The camera can take strings of photographs in quick succession. From two oblique photographs, taken from a slightly different angle, you can obtain a three-dimensional image of the target using a stereoscope.

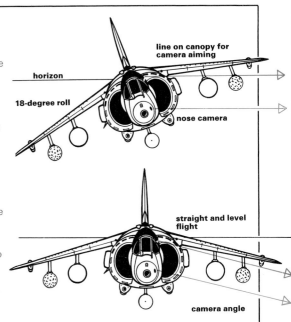

you quickly build up a 'mental library' of images and can recognise commonplace objects automatically. Identifying objects on an air photograph is based on five elements:

1 Size

Once you have established the scale of your photograph, you can ascertain the size of all objects shown. This obviously depends on the accuracy of the map from which you took the scale and whether the photo is of sufficient clarity to let you measure objects accurately. Enemy camouflage may be specifically designed to obscure the size of objects.

2 Shape

Some common objects have a very familiar shape, but others have to be classified as 'possible' and the alternatives eliminated by deduction. For example, a circular object seen on the ground could be a gas holder, oil tank, road roundabout, tent, sewage filter bed or even a round pond.

3 Shadow

The shape of any shadow cast by an object also helps you work out what it is. Its absence also tells you something. If, in the case of the example above, there is no shadow, the gas holder, oil tank or tent can be eliminated.

4 Tone

In general, objects with a smooth surface appear lighter in tone but rough surfaces are darker. So if the mysterious round object under consideration appears dark, then it is unlikely to be a road roundabout, which can be expected to appear in a light

tone. Only two possibilities are now left: the sewage bed (dark because of its rough clinker bed) or the round pond (which could show up light or dark).

5 Associated features

The final stage is to use your common sense. Having narrowed down the possibilities: what would you expect to see next to whatever you think it is? Supposing the object has two rectangular shapes next to it; they cast no shadow and are light in tone. A small

building close by. Since a sewage bed is likely to have a pump house with it and a number of settlement tanks, you can rule out the pond and conclude that the mystery shape is a sewage filter bed.

The example followed through here is very straightforward. In practice, life will not always be so easy but the procedure is the same. Follow the stages to produce a variety of possible identifications, then narrow them down by deduction.

Tips on identifying objects

Railways

These appear as dark, narrow bands. Curves are gentle and are separated by straight sections. Tunnels can be numerous in hilly country: the line stops abruptly and resumes a little further on, following a similar alignment. Where two lines meet at a junction, they do so gradually and eventually merge. Unlike roads, there will be no right-angled junctions. Embankments or cuttings will appear frequently, their presence revealed by shadows.

Roads

Main roads are wider than railways and usually appear lighter in tone. They twist and turn in an irregular manner. Sharpness of the curves distinguishes them from railways, and junctions are more frequent.

Canals

These show as a thick, dark line with long, straight sections and gentle curves. They will be frequently crossed by bridges and will obviously follow the contours. Locks will appear where they traverse a slope.

Rivers

These are similar in tone to canals, but their courses are more irregular and will cut across contours rather than follow them.

Bridges

You can generally spot these as they cross water bodies, roads, railways etc. The type of bridge can usually be determined by its shadow. Pontoon bridges can be revealed by their floats.

Built-up areas

Different buildings are usually easy to recognise, but remember that older parts of cities tend to have narrower, winding streets. Many older European cities will have traces of fortifications.

Vegetation

Deciduous trees generally appear lighter in tone than conifers, and their tops will be bigger and fluffy in appearance. Growing crops tend to darken in tone as they get higher; bare earth fields show almost white, whereas fully grown barley or wheat will appear nearly black. Marshes appear similar, but look for streams criss-crossing them and look at the surrounding area. Crops with large leaves, like cabbages, will appear lighter than those with small leaves. Root crops are planted in regular rows as opposed to the solid mass of grain crops. Mixed crops, like allotments and market gardens, will look like a patchwork quilt. Scrubland and heath will appear mottled, since different-sized bushes are growing at irregular intervals above low grass, which shows as a light grey.

WET NIGHT AT WOODBURY

*A Marine **SNCO** builds the frame work for a hasty **OP** overlooking the valley in which the coming exercise will be run. This type of **OP** can be constructed quickly and is very effective in the short term.*

*Digging in an **OP** with full overhead protection is easily a full weekend's work. To save time the instructors make use of the remains of a suitably sited old fire trench.*

A training weekend in the Lympstone area has been scheduled for RMR Bristol. Unlike regulars, reservists are civilians first and soldiers second. There are always those who are unable to show because of work commitments. As it is the height of summer, some are away on holiday.

Stores distributed

By 2000hrs a few reservists have arrived at the RMR hut inside Lympstone's Commando Training Centre. A senior NCO takes charge as stores are sorted and distributed.

"You two – start opening those ration boxes. And you lot outside! Get in here and start doing something!"

Two minutes later, nine cartons have been opened and 90 'rat packs' neatly stacked. Another SNCO walks past.

"Don't open all those boxes!"

You pause. The sergeant enlightens you.

"We don't yet know how many people are turning up, do we? And all these cartons have to be accounted for so *don't* open any more!"

"Yes, Sergeant."

A short while later, those present are issued with a sleeping bag, SLR and sling, magazines, cleaning kit, a ration-pack and box of hexamine tablets.

"Are you on your first weekend of

Just when you thought it was safe to venture on to the radio net, having mastered basic voice procedure and the rudiments of the PRC 349 and 351, the staff tell you about BATCO.

Phase One?'' a bloody-minded SNCO asks a bewildered-looking recruit.

"Yes, Sergeant."

"Have you got a cooker?'

A what? You mean, they're not going to be issued?

"Er . . . no, Sergeant."

"*Why not*? Bloody tough then! You're gonna eat cold rations this weekend, aren't you?''

"Yes, Sergeant,'' agrees the recruit.

The SNCO strides off. The recruit stares after him, thinking to himself, "Cold rations? I'll borrow my mate's cooker."

Everyone smiles at the recruit's plight. Their smug grins tell watching instructors: "We've remembered to bring *our* cookers, Sergeant!'' Actually, about half of you are now desperately thinking, "Where the bloody hell can I find a cooker before *I'm* pinged?"

The more the merrier

At 23.25 hrs those of you undergoing Phase One training climb aboard a waiting four-tonner and leave for the training area at nearby Woodbury Common. At 23.59 those on Phase Two, along with three candidate NCOs, begin moving out on foot. At that moment a coach arrives carrying those from the Poole detachment.

There is a few minutes' delay while the RMR hut is unlocked and the Poole reservists are issued their kit. Another two men have left messages to say they will arrive in the morning.

The move on foot to the training area takes you along narrow country lanes and across rough, gorse-covered land. It begins to rain, and you are

Right: The signals exercise, PRC 349 strapped to the shoulder. Here a recruit is shown the correct way to wear the radio harness which is almost as much of a challenge to the intellect as BATCO itself.

Below: Soldiering has become an increasingly complex skill and in the Reserve they do not have the luxury of teaching all the skill as per the book. You have a few hours to master what the regular Marines are taught over a period of weeks. First lesson of the weekend is given at 0745 by one of the regular NCOs.

After fitting the 349 to your person you need to fit the throat microphone. The 349 is usually used for fireteam and section comms. Depending on the terrain it has a range of 3 or 4 kilometres and a good deal further if conditions are ideal.

The headset fits over one ear only so you can listen to what is going on in the outside world with the other. To operate the radio all you have to do is press in the switch on the lead to the throat mike.

soon soaked to the skin. Most of you revel in it, however. For those for whom soldiering is not a full-time occupation, marching at night in pouring rain is a great novelty. The more wet and muddy you become the happier you feel!

Stand-to

You reach your bivvy position in the early hours of Saturday morning, just in time for stand-to at first light! An SNCO, who has crept forward to observe your standard operational procedures in a harbour position, is quietly pleased with what he sees –

until he notices some of you wandering about without kit or weapons. He launches a lone attack, hurling thunderflashes into the startled camp. To your credit, a few have the presence of mind to return fire.

After stand-down, clearance patrols are sent out. The rest of the morning is taken up largely by revision lectures

Before any operation, weapons must be test fired: especially GPMGs, as you can't afford stoppages on a weapon that represents 90 per cent of the section's fire power. But don't test-fire just before you go out on patrol: it tells the enemy you're coming.

on the use of range cards, and on radio operating and voice procedure.

Many RMR instructors are former regulars with a wealth of practical experience. You pay careful attention to their every word, taking note of the main details during each lecture. Those of you undergoing Phase Two training will need to take in as much as possible if you are to qualify for the coveted green beret.

Practical lessons

Where appropriate, lectures are followed by a practical lesson. In addition to the NCO and SNCO instructors, you are assisted here by three trained soldiers – candidates preparing for their junior NCO cadre. The lectures give them an opportunity to brush up their own knowledge of a subject, while learning the basics of dealing with junior ranks. You are respectful of these young Marines who are sufficiently experienced to be considered for that precious first stripe, whereas *you* still have some way to go before you can call yourself a trained soldier. Still, within a couple of years, you could be a corporal yourself. . . .

Temporary hide

While you struggle to grasp the essentials of signalling, two more instructors hastily construct a temporary hide. A convenient shell scrape is found in just the right place, overlooking a valley you are to observe during the afternoon's field exercise. After clearing the old dug-out of any debris, the SNCOs construct a framework of branches. Over this they secure sufficient foliage to blend in the position with its surroundings. The job is soon finished.

Of course, a more long-term hide could take days to build, but this at least provides you with an idea on the principles of constructing a very basic OP.

Combat Report
Vietnam:
Tet Offensive Engagement

David Dove was on his second tour in Vietnam when the Tet Offensive of January 1968 brought enemy combat troops storming in to try to overrun a previously "safe" rear-area base. At Dove's US Army airfield, a firefight raged all night.

The roof of the Quonset hut came falling in on top of us. There was smoke and debris everywhere. Somebody was screaming. We'd kept our rifles next to our bunks, although the war had seemed miles away. A couple of medics came in and told us that NVA mortars were dropping everywhere and that those of us who weren't injured should get the hell out. Some of the guys in our compound had been at a movie shown outdoors behind the mess hall, Dustin Hoffman in "The Graduate." I learned later that in the first moments of the attack mortar rounds came in dead-centre, killing three guys.

Minutes later, at just 11 p.m., two battalions of NVA attacked our airfield near Ban Me Theot. Our guys guarding the perimeter were all but wiped out in the first few minutes. The First Shirt – our first sergeant – rounded up a bunch of us mechanics, electricians and maintenance guys and told us to take positions in a zigzag trench facing the south perimeter where the attack was centred. I started off in that direction on my own, and more NVA mortar rounds exploded just behind me.

The base was on fire

"Get down in here!" somebody yelled. A helicopter mechanic, Peterson, was slumped in a shell crater beside the mess hall. "Come on, take cover!"

Flares and illumination grenades were going off, casting a blinding glare on the barbed wire marking the south perimeter, where the NVA were coming through. I clambered down behind Peterson and braced my rifle. I didn't want him to know I was so scared I'd lost control of my bodily functions.

"Better start learning to talk Vietnamese, Dave, because we're about to get overrun."

Four hundred NVA were pouring through the outer fences at three locations, some of them no more than half a klick from where Peterson and I, bending over our M16s, were popping off at their black silhouettes backlighted by bursting flares. The base was on fire. Shrapnel whipped through the air and I saw two of our mess hall cooks, oblivious to the risk, trying to set up an M60 machine-gun on flat ground.

In less than an hour of hard pushing, a number of NVA broke through the barbed wire and were inside the compound. The guys manning that trench had to pick up and pull out under pointblank fire. But then the NVA bogged down. Apparently our own artillery was beginning to do some damage behind them at the treeline. Peterson and I fired several clips and were pretty sure we knocked down some of the ones who were already inside the fence.

The First Shirt sent our orderly room clerk, Cox – now transformed into a fearsome soldier with M79 grenade-launcher and harness belts loaded with rounds – to tell us that we were going to abandon the mess hall area and pull back. The First Shirt himself was a bulky old guy, highly visible because he was wearing a white T-shirt, and he was shooting at the attackers with a .45 pistol gripped in both hands.

The face-to-face firefight went on for nearly three hours. Several times, those stocky NVA troopers actually did get close enough for us to see their faces in the yellow glare. I have to hand it to them, they were one bunch of brave sons of bitches.

In this kind of situation, there's too much confusion for the conflict to seem "personal". But there was one moment when I actually saw my rifle bullets double a man over and send him down. I even heard what sounded like a grunt as he hit the dirt. Then, with Peterson and Cox, I followed the sarge's advice and pulled back.

I functioned mechanically

We retreated to the rows of Quonset buildings, including my own "home", which had been wrecked. Cox handled his M79 like a six-shooter from the Wild West. I saw one grenade blast pick up several North Vietnamese and fling them aside like discarded trash.

In this kind of situation, there's no time to ponder what's happening. Once past my initial fright, I functioned more or less mechanically, setting up a relay to pass fresh ammo along to some guys down the line and using my own M16 intermittently, being careful to shoot only when I thought I had a clear target.

At one point we had a close-up view of a couple of dozen silhouettes of NVA soldiers who were getting very, very near to us. "We can't hold out against this," I was thinking. The air was thick with the stench of burnt cordite and there were expended shell casings everywhere.

"There's some aircraft coming in to help," someone said.

We were mobbed together – not a good idea; we made a good target – pulling back to a row of sandbags along the buildings. "The jets can't get in here at night," the First Shirt pointed out. "And there ain't no gunships in the area."

"No, these are Spads. They're comin'."

"Spads?" I inquired.

"Skyraiders, actually." This was the prop-driven Douglas A-1 Skyraider which could tote up to 12,000 lbs of bombs and seemed to be able to operate in darkness.

There were bodies everywhere

The NVA covered the ground we'd just abandoned. Then we heard engines and sensed the aircraft passing overhead, though we didn't actually see them. There were explosions some distance away, nowhere near the NVA who were already inside the compound, but they must have done enough damage to convince the enemy to call off the fight: they started pulling back to the barbed wire.

Eventually, we occupied the trench which had been our objective at the beginning. We were still shooting at an occasional NVA for an hour or more after that, until we could see the first hint of dawn in the distant sky.

Sunrise brought the most horrible scene I've ever witnessed, one that caused me to forget being ill, weary, hungry and soiled. There were bodies strewn everywhere. Dead men littered the ground between the trench and the fence, and at various locations all over our compound with its adjacent airfield. Someone eventually counted 47 dead NVA. Nineteen of our guys had been killed and a similar number wounded. The NVA had destroyed several buildings and two Huey helicopters and a Beaver airplane on the ground.

We learned later that ours was a "minor" engagement compared to other actions in the Tet Offensive sweeping the country. It may have been "minor", but I still get a spasm in my stomach when I think about it.

Firing from the perimeter at suspicious movement on the other side of the wire. The VC often used agents within US bases to discover the defensive layout and plan the best assault route.

841

BATTLE IN THE FERNS

The patrol moves very cautiously forward as it approaches the area of the OP. The lead scout advances, weapon in the shoulder, constantly covering his arc as he moves.

At midday on the Saturday of your RMR training weekend, you move away from the harbour area for the field exercise phase. You are split into three groups – two fire teams (Charlie and Delta) and a five-man observation post party. The fire teams are detailed to move into a lying-up position while the OP goes in to observe an area known to have been infiltrated by the enemy.

The approach is made along a series of rough tracks cut through the bush and gorse-land of Woodbury Common. Despite it being a mid-summer afternoon it begins to rain – a trickle at first, and then a downpour. Nobody says so, but the novelty of getting cold

and wet is finally beginning to wear a bit thin!

While the fire teams settle in, the OP party crawls towards their prepared hide. The instructors observe the proceedings, occasionally offering a word of advice. The first man wriggles his way into the camouflaged position, followed closely by another. So far, so good. Then, as the second man is crawling past the hide, his webbing snags on a branch – part of the over-

A Marine moves warily in to the OP. If you are compromised at this stage you could receive an unwelcome visit: OPs are not easily defended, and rarely have all-round vision.

head cover. The entire construction promptly collapses around the Marine already inside.

Despite the hilarious spectacle, the instructors try not to laugh (much) and are quick to repair the worst of the damage. They prop up the overhead cover sufficiently for the two men to see through it. In fact, the new hide now looks more natural than the original version.

A third member of the party now takes up a sentry position while the other two put up a poncho shelter beneath some nearby bushes. Satisfied, the instructors leave the recruits to carry on with their tasks.

A sentry covers the rear of the **OP** so that the occupants can concentrate on what is going on down in the valley without worrying about watching their backs. The novelty value of being drenched is obviously wearing a bit thin with this sentry.

The long wait

Amid intermittent downpours, the fire teams and OP remain concealed for nearly three hours. Nobody knows how much longer you will have to stay in position. It could be for the rest of the day. It could even be all night.

The uncomfortable pair crouching in the muddy OP shift and fidget restlessly, their eyes straining for signs of enemy activity in the valley below. Suddenly, there is movement along a track leading past a prominent clump of bushes some 150 metres distant. A couple enjoying a stroll in between the torrential rains? A man out walking his dog? Not this time.

Several figures, wearing camouflage smocks and carrying rifles, are seen moving from right to left, off the track, and into the undergrowth at its edge.

The OP relays this information to the patiently waiting fire teams. They then form as a fighting patrol and move forward, under cover of head-high ferns and shrubs. They advance almost to the edge of a clearing to within less than 50 metres from the enemy position.

When the attack goes in, everything happens very quickly indeed. Using red and green smoke for cover, Charlie and Delta fire teams assault the position from two sides, leapfrogging forward using the latest SA80 tactics.

The instructors seem to be everywhere at once, shouting advice and encouragement in between giving orders:

"Okay, let's go!"

"Charlie Fire Team, *move now*!"

"You, gunner – watch where you're firing, pay attention to what's happening around you . . . If you can't bloody see, then change position!"

"Okay, Delta Fire Team, *move*!"

"Fight through the position. . .!"

Moments later it is over. While a cover party looks on, a search party goes in and hurriedly checks the

Above: Having got the word from the OP, the fire teams move off to dig out the enemy. Try to get as close as possible using stealth: if you go in making a lot of noise you will waste time and ammunition firing and manoeuvring forward for longer than necessary.

Above and right: When in contact with the enemy, half of you must be putting down accurate fire while the other half dashes forward; otherwise you will take casualties. It sounds simple enough, but it is difficult in rough country where you can't see everyone all the time.

Fighting Fit

"enemy" casualties. All are dead. Of course in a real situation the bodies would be relieved of official papers, personal letters and diaries. You would remove or destroy their weapons and ammunition and, depending on the circumstances, salvage equipment and rations.

Back to life

With the enemy regarded as searched, the fire teams are ordered to withdraw, back across the clearing, and into the ferns.

"Through the track ... that track there! In single file. Come on men, *pay attention to detail!*"

Silence again descends over the valley. The "enemy" now come to life, brush themselves down and move off towards the next position to be attacked. The OP remains where it is, while the fire teams return to harbour positions to await further orders and be debriefed on the assault. Then you switch roles. Others take their turn at manning an OP, while those from the initial OP have a go at operating as part of a fire team.

At about 1700 hours, another similar attack is carried out against an enemy-occupied OP in a nearby wooded area.

That evening, orders and rehearsals precede a 2½-hour recce patrol. At 01.00 hrs, while en route back to the harbour area, you run into a carefully prepared ambush. Following a crash-move to a new position you bivvy up for what remains of the night.

On Sunday morning you are faced with a six-mile "out of contact" speed march. The route takes you back to CTCRM – where all is still not yet over. Everyone is now required to

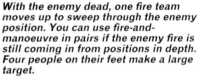

Right: If you lose your gunner during an assault you are in real trouble. When he is moving, the riflemen in the fire team must put down rapid fire to cover him. If he is hit, you must get the GPMG back into operation.

undergo various tests involving rope work. Climbing up a 30-ft rope might not sound like much – until you have spent two nights with little sleep, then had to double several miles carrying weapons and equipment! However, this is what you joined for.

"It's hard sometimes," confirms Marine Halley of the Plymouth Detachment. "It can be tough ... but I enjoy it!"

With the enemy dead, one fire team moves up to sweep through the enemy position. You can use fire-and-manoeuvre in pairs if the enemy fire is still coming in from positions in depth. Four people on their feet make a large target.

Above: The successful attack over, you beat a hasty retreat: enemy positions have a nasty habit of being DFs. Again, one group covers while the other moves, just in case.

Left: There is just time after recce patrol orders for rehearsals, which cover all the essentials including action on ambush. Just as well, in view of what the enemy has planned for the evening.